The road ahead is a spiritual journey. You begin your journey when you accept Jesus Christ as your Savior. At that moment, you are promoted from the ranks of the lost into the army of the found. Jesus puts your feet on the solid ground of His provision, and points you in the direction of His will. He gives you a permanent, indwelling travel guide in the presence of the Holy Spirit. The Lord strengthens you for the journey with His grace, protection, and love. He makes sure you are well-equipped for every mountain, battle, valley, and celebration. Jesus never removes His eyes from you. You are the object of His unfailing love, and He will not allow your foot to slip or falter. Because of Christ, your final destination is sure. He is anticipating your arrival and preparing a place for you in eternity.

At the beginning of your journey, you may take baby steps, struggling with your sin, your weakness, and your fear of the unknown. As you watch God work in your life, and experience His grace and compassion, you will eventually begin to surrender much more to Him. You will unclench the fists that hold on so tightly, and give their contents over to the Lord. You will trust Him with tomorrow. You will begin to live in the peace that comes from knowing and loving our God. There are rewards for faithful living, some of them received here, but most reserved for heaven. One of the rewards comes from obedience and commitment. It is the satisfaction of knowing you are pursuing godliness and pleasing your Father.

The journey is about becoming more like the Lord. It is a high calling. The goal is to bring Him glory and honor, and represent Him well on earth. One day, you and I will run into the presence of the Lord and He will welcome us home with a celebration like we've never known. His pleasure will be our glory. His joy will be our crown. So press on toward the calling and keep your eyes on the destination. We're going to look at the journey of Abraham and focus on the road ahead, to see what it looks like to grow up in Jesus.

THE ROAD AHEAD
PART ONE

VIEWING

Genesis 12:1-4

[1]Now the Lord said to Abram,

"Go forth from your country,
And from your relatives,
And from your father's house,
To the land which I will show you;
[2]And I will make you a great nation,
And I will bless you
And make your name great;
And so you shall be a blessing;
[3]And I will bless those who bless you,
And the one who curses you I will curse.
And in you all the families of the earth shall be blessed."

[4]So Abram went forth as the Lord had spoken to him; and Lot went with him. Now Abram was seventy-five years old when he departed from Haran.

Genesis 12:10-13

[10]Now there was a famine in the land; so Abram went down to Egypt to sojourn there, for the famine was severe in the land. [11]And it came about when he came near to Egypt, that he said to Sarai his wife, "See now, I know that you are a beautiful women; [12]and it will come about when the Egyptians see you, that they will say, 'This is his wife'; and they will kill me, but they will let you live. [1]"Please say that you are my sister so that it may go well with me because of you, and that I may live on account of you."

Genesis 22:1-3

[1]Now it came about after these things, that God tested Abraham, and said to him, "Abraham!" And he said, "Here I am." [2]And He said, "Take now your son, your only son, whom you love, Isaac, and go to the land of Moriah; and offer him there as a burnt offering on one of the mountains of which I will tell you." [3]So Abraham rose early in the morning and saddled his donkey, and took two of his young men with him and Isaac his son; and he split wood for the burnt offering, and arose and went to the place of which God had told him.

Genesis 25:7-8

[7]And these are all the years of Abraham's life that he lived, one hundred and seventy-five years. [8]And Abraham breathed his last and died in a ripe old age, an old man and satisfied with life; and he was gathered to his people.

DESTINATION

PRINCIPLES FOR MAKING LIFE'S JOURNEY COUNT

DAVID EDWARDS

LIFEWAY PRESS
NASHVILLE, TN

ISBN 0-7673-2603-2
Dewey Decimal Classification: 248.4
Subject Heading: DISCIPLESHIP

Unless otherwise noted, Scripture quotations are from the
New American Standard Bible.
©The Lockman Foundation, 1960, 1962, 1963, 1968, 1971, 1973, 1975, 1977. Used by permission.

Author: David Edwards
Writer: Angela Guffey

Cover Design: Tom Davis
Photography: Jeff Frasier
Art Direction: Edward Crawford

Printed in the United States of America

LifeWay Press
127 Ninth Avenue, North
Nashville, Tennessee 37234

contents

meet David Edwards

David Edwards travels the country full-time speaking for churches, schools, rallies, conferences, revivals, and camps. A native of Oklahoma City, Oklahoma, David holds a Bachelor of Arts degree in religion from Oklahoma City University. He has also completed graduate work toward a degree from Southwestern Baptist Theological Seminary.

A gifted communicator, David speaks from his heart about issues relevant to Generation X.

In January 1994, David began a weekly, citywide young adult Bible study in Houston, Texas. This study, hosted by First Baptist Church, Houston, has grown from 45 to 1500 young adults in three years. Regardless of the setting, whether in the pulpit; on stage at a summer camp; in a large arena; at a citywide, young adult Bible study; for a seminar; or a school program, David has a heart for young adults. A member of Generation X himself, David knows firsthand the world of this generation. He helps them discover the importance of a Christ-centered lifestyle. David masterfully applies Biblical truths to the current issues of the day in an honest, humorous, and understandable form.

David's goal in ministry is to meet young adults where they are in life and bring them one step closer to knowing and becoming like Jesus Christ.

introduction

Welcome to my world, or what has become my world over the last eight years. It all started when I apprenticed with two evangelists. They helped me understand the value of character and consistency in my personal life. I lived in Georgia for a time, staying in an old converted chicken coop for five dollars a week. I would drive out from there and speak in many different settings: churches, colleges, school assemblies, camps, and conferences. In the course of one week, I would speak seven or eight times to every possible age group. I found the more I did, the more there was to do.

Someone once told me, "You can only have the ministry the church will let you have." Well, the church has been good to me. Three years ago I began a Bible study for young single adults. We started with 45 people and in three years have grown to 1500. Young adults have come to the study from every background imaginable. It has become a doorway for many adults to come to Christ, and for others to reconnect with Him. All along, God has been crafting a message in me—to reintroduce the gospel to my generation.

Since living in the chicken coop in Atlanta, I've consistently been on the road. Last year I spoke 510 times and flew 110,000 miles. For me, the road has been a slow and steady discovery of one very freeing truth. The truth is that life is a journey and a process. In other words, the way life is now is not the way it will always be.

There are two ways to approach the journey, as a tourist or a traveler. A tourist is someone who passes through places but gets very little out of it. They are spectators and spend their lives looking at others, looking at situations, but never really becoming a part of it. At one time or another, we've all been tourists. We go to an event, enjoy it, say, "That was fun while it lasted," and move on.

Then there are travelers. They are the people who know what it means to live wherever they are. They aren't waiting for something better to come along to start living. Travelers listen, hear, love, feel, and experience every place in life. Travelers leave part of themselves behind because they invests their lives in others. They are also richer for the journey because they allow others to invest in them. Wasn't that Jesus' great commandment to go and invest our lives? My life has been shaped by the people who've invested in me, and the places I've been.

So when the journey gets rough, and it will, and you want to beat yourself up because of mistakes, or you just want to quit, remind yourself that it's a process. You are not at the destination yet. There is grace to fuel your journey. The elements that guide the journey are the principles of God's Word. Those principles are always true, they're always consistent, and when we lose our direction, they point us back toward Him. But the principles must be applied by the traveler. They have no power unless they're applied. So as one traveler to another, I have enclosed some principles for study and application to make your journey count.

Happy traveling. See you at the destination.

David

The Road Ahead

THE
ROAD
AHEA
D

1

"THEREFORE LEAVING THE
ELEMENTARY TEACHING ABOUT
THE CHRIST, LET US PRESS ON
TO MATURITY

(HEBREWS 6:1).

GUIDE

1. Abraham follows God for . . . .
   (Genesis 12:1-4)

Initially we come to Him for . . . .

The danger is . . . .

2. Abraham faces the reality of his weakness. (Genesis 12:10-13)

Christianity is not God's attempt to limit you, but to . . . .

Our weaknesses sabotage . . . .

Power is perfected in . . . .
(2 Corinthians 12:9)

(The Road Ahead Viewing Guide continues on page 19.)

Discussion Questions

1. What are the benefits of following God?

2. What weakness could you deal with that would produce the biggest change in your life?

ABRAHAM FOLLOWS GOD
GOING THE EXTRA MILE
FOR RESULTS-SALVATION

Initially, Abraham followed God for what he could get. It took promises to get him to obey. It's okay to start here, but you can't stay here. The danger of staying here is that you get selfish.

When God called Abraham, He made many promises to him. Read Genesis 12:1-4 below and underline all God promised Abraham.

We all begin our journey similar to Abraham. We see the benefits of salvation, and we want all it has to offer.

Now the Lord said to Abram, "Go forth from your country, and from your relatives, and from your father's house, to the land which I will show you; And I will make you a great nation, and I will bless you and make your name great; and so you shall be a blessing; and I will bless those who bless you, and the one who curses you I will curse. And in you all the families of the earth shall be blessed." So Abram went forth as the Lord had spoken to him; and Lot went with him. Now Abram was seventy-five years old when he departed from Haran (Genesis 12:1-4).

Look at some of the results of our salvation:

acceptance with God
miss hell and make heaven
peace in our lives
hopefulness
prayer with the Father
new moral goals
victory
new horizons
self-fulfillment
unconditional love of Jesus
forgiveness
receive the Holy Spirit
courage to face tomorrow
joy
guidance from the Father
freedom
new thoughts
convictions
new community with Christians

DAVE
QUOTE

If all your past does is to drive you to the presence of God, then it's served its purpose. That's the point.

What were the things at work in your life that brought you to Christ?

. . . .

. . . .

What results have you seen?

. . . .

. . . .

. . . .

Sometimes we come to Christ because this is the last stop. We've tried everything else. Nothing else has worked. But that's OK.

Many of us still have some issues about our salvation.

Was I really saved back in the third grade? Do I need to accept Christ again, in case I didn't do it right the first time? Can I lose my salvation?

Take a look at the gospel—what it is, how it affects our lives, and what the results are.

The Results of Our Salvation Based on the Gospel

WHAT HAPPENED TO JESUS	HAPPENS TO US	AND PRODUCES IN US
Crucifixion Jesus died on a cross as payment for our lives.	**Crucified with Christ** We come to the end of ourselves, surrender our will and believe that His death is payment for our lives.	**Confidence** It is no longer confidence in our goodness or badness but in the cross.
Resurrection Christ Jesus is placed in a tomb. He beats death—comes back out of the tomb with resurrection life.	**Resurrected with Christ** When we believe, that same resurrection life is placed in us.	**Reason** Because of the resurrection, the reason to live isn't about you anymore. It is about His life in you.
Ascension He goes up to be seated at the right hand of God. A place of authority.	**Ascended with Christ** Because He is in control, that authority gives us the ability to do His will.	**Ability** We no longer have to operate in our own strength or be afraid of the challenges.

If you still question the most important decision in your life, now's the time to nail it down. You can't take one step toward maturity if you doubt your salvation. If you know for sure you have accepted

Christ as your Savior, then skip ahead to the next section. If you want to get this straight with God, then PRAY a prayer like this, or pray with a friend who knows Jesus:

I know I am separated from You. I ask You to forgive me. I believe You died for me. I now turn my life over to You as the leader of my heart and my life. In Jesus' name, Amen.

Because of your salvation, your destination is secure. Turn to each of these verses to read about the security of your salvation.

Jude 24 — God's power is able to keep a believer.

John 10:28-29 — No one can seize the believer from his safe position, even yourself.

John 6:39-40 — Christ's death was enough; if something can undo our salvation then Christ's death was not enough.

1 John 2:1 — Christ is our advocate when Satan wants to condemn us for our sin.

Ephesians 4:30 — We are sealed by the Holy Spirit until the day of redemption, not until the day of sinning.

PRAY a prayer of thanksgiving. Thank God for your salvation. Thank Him for holding onto you even when you turn away from Him.

ABRAHAM FACES THE REALITY OF
GOING THE EXTRA MILE
HIS WEAKNESS–SIN NATURE

Abraham ran from difficulty and conflict. In Genesis 12, he was faced with famine and ran to Egypt. In Egypt, Abram lied to Pharaoh. He told Pharaoh that Sarah was his sister, hoping he would favor Sarah and treat him well. All did go well for awhile. Abram became wealthy, but his scheme nearly lost him his wife. God divinely intervened, saved Abram and Sarah, and delivered them from Egypt. Later in chapter 20, Abraham tells the same lie to Abimelech, the king of Gerar. Abraham finally has to face up to his sin. Again, God intervenes and protects the marriage and His promise to make a great nation from Abraham.

We are so much like Abraham. We too are called to follow. Then in the light of God, compared to His holiness, we are confronted with our sin and weak places. As God begins to reveal the depth of our sin and the weaknesses that plague us, our responsibility as growing believers is to deal with the issues in godly ways. Not all weakness is sin. But when God brings it up, it's time to deal with it. It makes you stronger and produces real Christianity. Relationships become stronger.

So, if all weaknesses aren't sin, then what is sin?

"Indeed there is not a righteous man on earth who continually does good and who never sins" (Ecclesiastes 7:20).

"Who can say, 'I have cleansed my heart, I am pure from my sin?' " (Proverbs 20:9).

DEFINITION OF SIN

Sin is anything that separates you from God's purpose and God's presence.

Hardness of heart and unbelief are at the core of sinfulness. It means refusing to repent and believe in the promises of God. It's a stubborn unwillingness to be open to the love of God. Other manifestations of sin include pride, sensuality, fear, self-pity, selfishness, jealously, greed, and fear.

Take a look at these verses. The Bible affirms that sin is universal. No one is excluded.

"For all have sinned and fall short of the glory of God" (Romans 3:23).

In what areas do you find yourself frequently being pulled away from God?

. . . .

Display of Sin

When faced with our sin, we can respond in healthy or unhealthy ways. The unhealthy response is to continue to display your sin—talk about it, rearrange it, mess with it—but never really deal with it. Have you ever heard yourself say or think any of these unhealthy things?

"It's all my fault. Everything I do is wrong. I can't seem to do anything to please God."—obsessive guilt over your mistakes

"There's nothing wrong here. It's just the way I am."—denial

"I've been struggling with this for years. I'm waiting on God to do something."—wallowing

"What difference does it make? I can always get forgiveness."—continuing in sin; refusing to take responsibility

"When's it ever going to get better? Why did this happen to me? I should just quit."—victim mentality

in is like a bad wheel on a grocery art—it always pulls in one direction. Sin continually pulls you away rom God's purposes.

DAVE QUOTE

Dealing with Sin

Psalm 51 is David's journal account of a healthy response to sin:
¹Be gracious to me, O God, according to Thy lovingkindness;
According to the greatness of Thy compassion blot out my transgressions.
²Wash me thoroughly from my iniquity,
and cleanse me from my sin.
³For I know my transgressions,
and my sin is ever before me.
⁴Against Thee, Thee only, I have sinned,
And done what is evil in Thy sight,
So that Thou art justified when Thou dost speak,
And blameless when Thou dost judge.
⁵Behold, I was brought forth in iniquity,
And in sin my mother conceived me.
⁶Behold, Thou dost desire truth in the innermost being,
And in the hidden part Thou wilt make me know wisdom.
⁷Purify me with hyssop, and I shall be clean;
Wash me, and I shall be whiter than snow.
⁸Make me to hear joy and gladness,
Let the bones which Thou hast broken rejoice.
⁹Hide Thy face from my sins,
And blot out all my iniquities.
¹⁰Create in me a clean heart, O God,
And renew a steadfast spirit within me.
¹¹Do not cast me away from Thy presence,
And do not take Thy Holy Spirit from me.
¹²Restore to me the joy of Thy salvation,
And sustain me with a willing spirit.
¹³Then I will teach transgressors Thy ways,
and sinners will be converted to Thee.

Using the chart on page 16, walk through the steps of this passage in regard to your own sin and weak places.
Are there other positive steps you could take to deal with your sin and weak places (write a letter, make a phone call, or bring closure to some past area)?

. . . .

| Clear it up | Admit your sin —confess it | Verse 4—against the Lord have I sinned |

Spend some time clearing up your sin with the Lord. Confess that it is against Him that you have sinned.

| Clean it out | Turn from your sin —repent | Verse 10—create in me a clean heart |

Take time to think about new habits that could replace your old sin patterns. Ask the Lord for strength to turn from your sin. Ask Him for a clean heart.

| Carry on | Keep walking with God | Verse 12—restore the joy of salvation |

Remind yourself of the joy that came with your salvation.

| Carry out | Tell others about God | Verse 13—teach others about God's forgiveness |

Let the joy of God's forgiveness overflow to others. Tell them about His love and compassion. Tell them about the freedom that comes from dealing with sin in a healthy way.

DAVE QUOTE

Becoming like Christ means taking responsibility for my behavior.

PRAY this prayer if you don't even know where to start:

God I know I've blown it. Would You forgive me? Please give me the strength to get up and go forward. I want to do what pleases You. In Jesus' name, Amen.

Delivered from Sin

God is so good to us. He sent His Son to deliver us from our sin. His love and compassion are endless. Take a look at these passages to see how God responds.

"If we confess our sins, He is faithful and righteous to forgive us our sins and to cleanse us from all unrighteousness" (1 John 1:9).

"The Lord's lovingkindnesses indeed never cease,
   For His compassions never fail.
   They are new every morning;
   Great is Thy faithfulness"
(Lamentations 3:22-23).

"He will again have compassion on us;
   He will tread our iniquities under foot.
   Yes, Thou wilt cast all their sins
   Into the depths of the sea"
(Micah 7:19).

" 'And their sins and their lawless deeds I will remember no more' " (Hebrews 10:17).

Answer these questions from the above Scriptures—
What happens when we confess our sins? (see 1 John 1:9)

. . . .

How often will the Lord give you new compassion and a new start? (see Lamentations 2:22-23)

. . . .

Where does God put our sin? (see Micah 7:19)

. . . .

How long will God continue to remember your confessed sin? (see Hebrews 10:17)

. . . .

PRAY and thank God for His forgiveness. Thank Him for giving you each day with a clean slate. Thank Him for casting your sin into the depths of the sea and then posting a NO FISHIN' sign. Thank Him for remembering your sin no more.

TRAVEL-LOG

1. What principle or truth have you learned about the journey?

. . . .

. . . .

. . . .

. . . .

. . . .

2. What do you feel God is trying to say to you about your journey?

. . . .

. . . .

. . . .

. . . .

. . . .

3. What new steps can you take toward the destination (things to do, things to change, things to avoid)?

. . . .

. . . .

. . . .

THE ROAD AHEAD PART TWO

VIEWING

Genesis 12:1-4

[1]Now the Lord said to Abram,
   "Go forth from your country,
   And from your relatives,
   And from your father's house,
   To the land which I will show you;
   [2]And I will make you a great nation,
   And I will bless you
   And make your name great;
   And so you shall be a blessing;
   [3]And I will bless those who bless you,
   And the one who curses you I will curse.
   And in you all the families of the earth shall be blessed."
[4]So Abram went forth as the Lord had spoken to him; and Lot went with him. Now Abram was seventy-five years old when he departed from Haran.

Genesis 12:10-13

[10]Now there was a famine in the land; so Abram went down to Egypt to sojourn there, for the famine was severe in the land.
[11]And it came about when he came near to Egypt, that he said to Sarai his wife, "See now, I know that you are a beautiful women;
[12]and it will come about when the Egyptians see you, that they will say, 'This is his wife'; and they will kill me, but they will let you live.
[1]"Please say that you are my sister so that it may go well with me because of you, and that I may live on account of you."

Genesis 22:1-3

[1]Now it came about after these things, that God tested Abraham, and said to him, "Abraham!" And he said, "Here I am."
[2]And He said, "Take now your son, your only son, whom you love, Isaac, and go to the land of Moriah; and offer him there as a burnt offering on one of the mountains of which I will tell you."
[3]So Abraham rose early in the morning and saddled his donkey, and took two of his young men with him and Isaac his son; and he split wood for the burnt offering, and arose and went to the place of which God had told him.

Genesis 25:7-8

[7]And these are all the years of Abraham's life that he lived, one hundred and seventy-five years.
[8]And Abraham breathed his last and died in a ripe old age, an old man and satisfied with life; and he was gathered to his people.

GUIDE

3. Abraham's focus becomes . . . .
   (Genesis 22:1-3)
   What's missing from these verses? . . . .

   The emphasis is no longer on Abraham, but on . . . .

   God wants to get us to the point that we follow Him not for . . . .

   When you're more concerned about what God wants, then your faith has begun to

   . . . .

4. Abraham dies . . . .
   (Genesis 25:7-8)

Mature faith is accomplished through

. . . .

1. Have you been stuck in the same place on the road for too long? Why?
2. What does it mean that Abraham died satisfied with life?
3. How do you define satisfaction and contentment?
4. Are you committed to stay on the road?
5. Where would you place yourself on the road?

ABRAHAM'S FOCUS BECOMES

GOING THE EXTRA MILE

RIGHTEOUS-SURRENDER

Abraham began to learn about the character of God, and between Genesis 12 and 22, Abraham grew up. He began to make righteous choices. He responded in faith to God's instruction to offer his son Isaac as a burnt offering. Abraham surrendered his life to God, evidenced by his willingness to obey. He went to sacrifice his son because of what he believed about the character of God. Based on his confidence in God, he made a righteous choice.

God wants us to follow Him for who He is, not what He does. Righteous choices come from surrender to God. Righteous choices produce spiritual maturity. Each step along the road builds on another. The destination is the maturity of Christ. The goal is to look like Jesus. There is grace for the process. And like Abraham, we begin the journey by making righteous choices based on our confidence about who God is.

How do I make a righteous choice?

GETTING TO THE DESTINATION

THE DESTINATION
TO ATTAIN THE MATURITY OF CHRIST - EPHESIANS 4:13

⬆

CONSISTENCY

⬆

SPIRITUAL MATURITY

⬆

A WILLINGNESS TO MAKE RIGHTEOUS CHOICES

⬆

CONFIDENCE IN WHO GOD IS

1. A righteous choice honors eternal things — things that don't change, like:
   the person of God
   the passions of God
   the power of God

Are you facing any choices? How could you honor the eternal things of God in your decision?

. . . .

. . . .

2. A righteous choice must have consistent application.
   nothing without permission—
      Does it have God's approval?
   obedience regardless of the cost or benefit
   obedience openly, not ashamed

3. A righteous choice causes spiritual maturity.

A righteous choice is doing the right thing no matter what you feel or what you get.

DAVE QUOTE

DAVE QUOTE

Sometimes I'm asked, "I'm dating a guy and he's not a Christian. Is it OK?" No, because you don't have permission to do that.

What's competing for your choices?

Are there steps you can take to make more righteous choices? Describe them below.

. . . .

. . . .

. . . .

. . . .

Spiritual Maturity

What Spiritual Maturity Is Not. John MacArthur writes in his book, *Keys to Spiritual Growth,* that "Many people entertain mistaken ideas about what spiritual maturity involves. They're not growing as rapidly as they could, or they're caught on a level far below where they should be, because they misunderstand what spiritual maturity is and how one grows in grace." He goes on to list a few reminders to help keep us on track.

Spiritual maturity has nothing to do with our position in Christ — We are already seen as perfect because of His Son. *It's not about being perfect.*

Spiritual maturity has nothing to do with God's favor — God doesn't love us any more, the more spiritual we become. *God can't love you any more than He already does.*

Spiritual maturity has nothing to do with time — You can be 50 years old and be a spiritual infant. *Growing up is a choice you make.*

Spiritual maturity has nothing to do with knowledge — You can know lots of stuff and still not be conformed to Christ. *The truth must be applied.*

Spiritual maturity has nothing to do with activity — Busyness is not evidence of spiritual maturity. *Fourteen Bible Studies a week does not a mature person make.*

Spiritual maturity has nothing to do with prosperity — Material blessings may be allowed but do not evidence spiritual maturity. *God is an inside God—He transforms from the inside out.*[1]

Does one of these reminders jump out at you? Why?

. . . .

. . . .

A spiritually mature person is growing in his or her gifts — The gifts God gave you are becoming stronger and more focused.

A spiritually mature person has fruit on his or her tree — Others can tell that Jesus lives inside of you. They see it in your character and life.

What a Spiritually Mature Person Looks Like

Maturity is not mystical, a formula, or some big secret, but comes through understanding and practicing the principles given in God's Word. Maturity doesn't mean you finally get happy, it means you get more like Jesus.

A spiritually mature person has an intimate relationship with the Lord. — Being devoted to spiritual disciplines (prayer, meditation, Bible study, Scripture memorization, etc.) produces a mind and heart that is more Christlike.

A spiritually mature person is not like a child who is tossed about. — You have a biblical grid that filters the world and its philosophies. New ideas that don't line up with Scripture don't toss you around.

A spiritually mature person has discernment — You are able to distinguish good from evil. You are not satisfied to remain a baby in spiritual matters.

A spiritually mature person has changed — You don't look, act, feel, respond, or believe the same as you used to. You are different because of Christ.

Are there areas where you need to grow spiritually?

. . . .

What are some practical ways you could pursue maturity?

. . . .

. . . .

PRAY for God's discernment about your maturity. Ask Him to guide you through righteous choices and show you areas where you need to grow. Ask Him for a consistent walk of maturity. Thank Him for His faithfulness to you.

ABRAHAM IS FULL-ON
GOING THE EXTRA MILE
REWARDED-SATISFIED

Genesis 25:7-8 records that Abraham lived 175 years and died "satisfied with life." His earthly reward for obedience was satisfaction and contentment with life. How would you rate yourself on the contentment gauge below?

Read Philippians 4:11-13 for Paul's lesson on contentment:

11Not that I speak from want; for I have learned to be content in whatever circumstances I am.

12I know how to get along with humble means, and I also know how to live in prosperity; in any and every circumstance I have learned the secret of being filled and going hungry, both of having abundance and suffering need.

13I can do all things through Him who strengthens me.

Paul is speaking to the Philippian Christians. He tells them in verse 11 that changing circumstances did not affect the inner contentment he enjoyed.

How do you respond to change?

. . . .

What about "neutral change" like a lateral promotion, change in job description, or taking a new way home? Is it an adventure and a learning experience, or do you resist any change?

. . . .

. . . .

Look at verse 12. Paul says, "I have learned the secret." He means that he has been initiated by his experiences. He has learned the lesson of contentment from his experiences. He had probably learned that —
1. He could trust God;
2. Worrying and anxiousness were a waste of time;
3. Rewards weren't necessarily received here on earth.

EMPTY
Hate life. Want to stay in bed and eat chips. Ready to start taking hostages.

FULL
Life's not OK, but I won't retreat, because God is able.

What are some lessons you have learned from your experiences about contentment?

. . . .

. . . .

In verse 13, Paul says the reason he can handle poverty or great abundance is because Jesus gives him strength to do everything.

Is there an area of your life that needs the strength of Jesus? Explain.

. . . .

. . . .

. . . .

. . . .

. . . .

What has been your definition of contentment?

. . . .

. . . .

Based on this Scripture, how would you define contentment?

. . . .

. . . .

Some Myths About Contentment

"If I could just get out of this town, I'd be happy."

"A husband/wife would make my life really full."

"When I have a family that loves me, then I'll be ready to love other people."

"After I 'make it,' then I'm going to get out and start enjoying life."

"To say I'm content means that I have to settle. I'll have to give up my dreams."

"Contentment is for the weak at heart and the easily pleased."

Can you think of some other myths about contentment? Describe below.

. . . .

. . . .

. . . .

Contentment is not for the weak or the passive. It requires incredible faith that comes from maturity. There is strength in contentment. It's not a dream stealer. You aren't required to settle. Contentment means that you have a peace about God's purpose for you right now.

Peace is a gift from God (see Galatians 5) that comes with maturity. Philippians 4:7 even says that peace defies human understanding. The bottom line with contentment is that without it, you will wish your life away. You're always searching for something else to fill you up, when all you need is right before you.

PRAY for the Lord to give you peace and contentment. Thank Him that today was a part of His plan for you. Thank Him for having a purpose for your life. Thank Him in advance for the strength He will give you through peace and contentment.

"But godliness actually is a means of great gain, when accompanied by contentment, for we have brought nothing into the world, so we cannot take anything out of it either. And if we have food and covering, with these we shall be content" (1 Timothy 6:6-8).

1John MacArthur, Keys to Spiritual Growth (Tarrytown, New York: Fleming H. Revell Company, 1976), 14-16.

TRAVEL-LOG

1. What principle or truth have you learned about the journey?

. . . .

. . . .

. . . .

. . . .

2. What do you feel God is trying to say to you about your journey?

. . . .

. . . .

. . . .

. . . .

. . . .

3. What new steps can you take toward the destination (things to do, things to change, things to avoid)?

. . . .

. . . .

. . . .

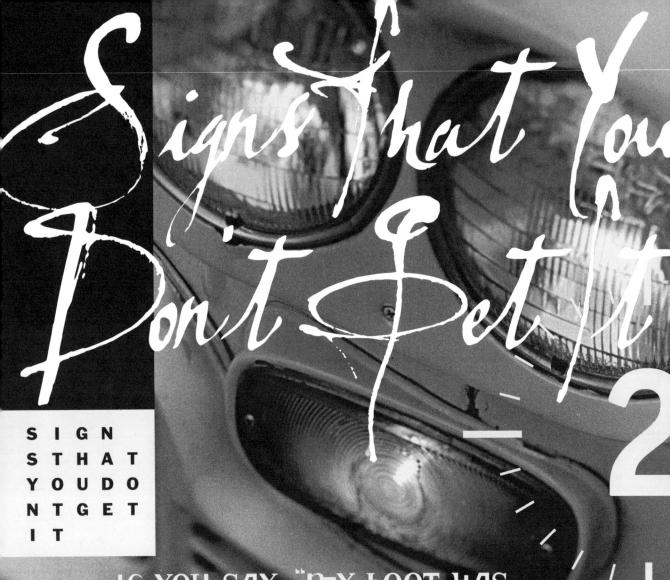

Signs That You Don't Get It

**SIGN
THAT
YOU DO
NT GET
IT**

2

IF YOU SAY, "MY bOOT HAS SLIPPED," THY LOVINGkindness, O Lord WILL HOLD ME UP (PSALM 94:18).

People who don't get it are people who've wandered off the main road. They may have been heading in the right direction, but for one reason or another have gotten side-tracked on their spiritual journey. Lots of things happen in our lives to get us off course. Bad directions. Wrong turns. Poor weather. Sometimes we get lost just because we don't pay attention to where we are going. When you lose your way, you aren't growing spiritually, and you may even be sliding backwards. However it happens, there are some signs to look for—ways to know you've lost sight of the destination.

We're going to take a look at Jesus, the Pharisees, and the disciples—a story full of people who don't get it. If you should see yourself in the next pages, don't run and hide. The good news is that Jesus is patient with His followers. His plans for you are not thwarted by wrong turns. He is bigger than the sum of your mistakes. So, if He whispers to you that you've gotten off course, quickly run to Him and let Him redirect your steps.

SIGNS THAT YOU GET IT ONE PART

VIEWING

Mark 8:14-21

14And they had forgotten to take bread; and did not have more than one loaf in the boat with them.

15And He was giving orders to them, saying, "Watch out! Beware of the leaven of the Pharisees and the leaven of Herod."

16And they began to discuss with one another the fact that they had no bread.

17And Jesus, aware of this, said to them, "Why do you discuss the fact that you have no bread? Do you not yet see or understand? Do you have a hardened heart?

18"Having eyes, do you not see? And having ears, do you not hear? And do you not remember,

19when I broke the five loaves for the five thousand, how many baskets full of broken pieces you picked up?" They said to Him, "Twelve."

20"And when I broke the seven for the four thousand, how many large baskets full of broken pieces did you pick up?" And they said to Him, "Seven."

21And He said to them, "Do you not yet understand?"

GUIDE

1. People who don't get it . . . .
   (Mark 8:15)

Jesus warned about the . . . .
of the Pharisees.

Leaven means . . . .

When you get preoccupied with what is not in your life, the first thing you sacrifice is . . . .

. . . .

Jesus was saying to the disciples, "Don't forget ...

. . . ."

The moment we allow Jesus to step out of Heaven and into our hearts, His Spirit acts in two ways -

as a . . . .

and as a . . . .

(Signs That You Don't Get It Viewing Guide continues on page 41.)

Discussion Questions

1. It's easier to hear God's voice when you know what you're listening for. What ways has God used to warn you about certain areas of your life?

2. We tend to trust God with our strengths and control our weaknesses. What areas are you still in control of?

FOCUSING ON
GOING THE EXTRA MILE
YOUR NEEDS

Some signs that you may have drifted off course:

- Focusing on your needs
- Holding on to stuff
- Quenching the Spirit
- Struggling with worry
- Missing the wonders of God

There is hope for all Pharisees and doubting disciples.

The disciples in Mark 8 were focused on their lack of bread and their need to eat. Self-centeredness caused them to lose their faith while the Bread of Life was right in the boat with them. They turned inward, saw their inadequacy to provide, and took their eyes off Jesus.

When we focus on our needs, we turn inward. We forget the lessons we have learned about God's provision. Focusing on ourselves prevents us from maturing. We stop pressing on and become paralyzed by our desires. Growth stops. We become spiritually stale.

Matthew 6:25-34 is Jesus' classic teaching on the provision of God. Let's work through these verses for more insight on trusting God.

25"Do not be anxious for your life, as to what you shall eat, or what you shall drink; nor for your body, as to what you shall put on. Is not life more than food, and the body than clothing? 26Look at the birds of the air, that they do not sow, neither do they reap, nor gather into barns, and yet your heavenly Father feeds them. Are you not worth much more than they? 27And which of you by being anxious can add a single cubit to his life's span? 28And why are you anxious about clothing? Observe how the lilies of the field grow; they do not toil nor do they spin, 29yet I say to you that even Solomon in all his glory did not clothe himself like one of these. 30But if God so arrays the grass of the field, which is alive today and tomorrow is thrown into the furnace, will He not much more do so for you, O men of little faith?

31Do not be anxious then, saying, 'What shall we eat?' or 'What shall we drink?' 'With what shall we clothe ourselves?' 32For all these things the Gentiles eagerly seek; for your heavenly Father knows that you need all these things. 33But seek first His kingdom and His righteousness; and all these things shall be added to you. 34Therefore do not be anxious for tomorrow; for tomorrow will care for itself. Each day has enough trouble of its own."

Underline every use of the word **anxious.**

What things are we not supposed to be anxious about?

. . . .

. . . .

Why is anxiousness a waste of time? (v. 27)

. . . .

on the Lord's provision. Satan says "get happy," but Jesus says, "get holy." Satan wants us to operate out of panic, instead of trust. He tries to get us to think things that aren't true. Following Satan off the path of godliness will only lead to a mirage where we may die in the desert, never reaching our final destination.

Can you think of other lies Satan uses to get us off the path? List them below.

. . . .

. . . .

. . . .

. . . .

What is the cause of our anxiousness? (v.30)

. . . .

Why can we trust God with our needs? (vv. 30,32)

. . . .

What are we supposed to do instead of worry? (v. 33)

. . . .

Many times it is tempting for us to try and meet our own needs, longings, and expectations. But if we do, then we are buying into a lie from Satan. He wants us to find satisfaction for ourselves instead of waiting

There is a way which seems right to a man, but its end is the way of death (Proverbs 14:12).

From Proverbs 14:12, will Satan's deception always be obvious and easily avoided? ❑ yes ❑ no

How can you always be sure to choose wisely? (See Matthew 6:33.)

. . . .

. . . .

Your priority shouldn't be personal happiness, but personal holiness, then God takes care of your needs.

What are some unmet needs that you are dealing with?

. . . .

. . . .

How is Satan trying to deceive you?

. . . .

What are some practical steps you can take to trust God with your needs?

. . . .

. . . .

DAVE QUOTE

To the same extent that you push aside the lies of Satan, you will see the blessings of God. To compromise with Satan is to also compromise on receiving the blessings of God.

PRAY for forgiveness for all the time you've spent being anxious. Surrender all your needs to God. Ask Him for strength and wisdom. Ask Him to deliver you from the tempting lines of Satan.

2

HOLDING ON
GOING THE EXTRA MILE
TO STUFF

The disciples held on to their one loaf of bread, and they held on to their need for provision. They had already learned twice that entrusting bread to Jesus meant multiplication and provision, but the disciples were immature followers who didn't get it. They hadn't learned the lesson of entrusting.

> To seek our personal happiness over God's will is like putting up a ROAD CLOSED sign over certain areas of our lives and asking God to work around it. We say, "Make me happy, but don't tell me who to date. Make me successful, but don't tell me how to spend my money."
>
> DAVE QUOTE

We Rarely Trust God With—
money
areas we're good at
timing
relationships
earthly future
free time
habits

We Willingly Trust God With—
weaknesses
eternity
things beyond our control
parking spots

We can be just like the disciples sometimes. We tend to compartmentalize our lives — things we'll trust God for, and things we'll struggle with on our own. Over the areas we hold on to, we post a big DO NOT ENTER sign. This matter is off limits to God and He isn't allowed there. What are some of the things you willingly trust God with?

. . . .

What areas are hardest to trust Him with?

. . . .

Is there something you have given to God and then taken back, over and over? ❏ yes ❏ no If so, describe below.

. . . .

. . . .

. . . .

. . . .

. . . .

What does Scripture say about holding on to stuff? Read the following for insight.

Cast your burden upon the Lord, and He will sustain you; He will never allow the righteous to be shaken (Psalm 55:22).

I know whom I have believed and I am convinced that He is able to guard what I have entrusted to Him until that day (2 Timothy 1:12).

Seek first His kingdom and His righteousness; and all these things shall be added to you (Matthew 6:33).

In regard to your stuff, Scripture says to cast, entrust, and seek God. *Entrusting* means transferring the responsibility of something valuable to a place of safe-keeping. To entrust God with everything means giving all the areas of your life to Him. You can stop worrying and fretting with your burdens. Your most valued possessions, relationships, dreams, and goals are much safer in the hands of God. He knows they are important to you. He will guard your treasure and assure its protection.

How do I begin to trust God with everything?

1. Reaffirm God's presence — His will is first. God has ownership over the specific. Dedicate those areas you struggle with to Him.

Pray. Take a specific area and dedicate it to the Lord. Reaffirm His ownership over that area. (Example — dating. Reaffirm the Lord's place in your dating life and rededicate that relationship to God.)

2. Recognize the process — Begin with the areas you can easily give up and then relinquish the rest as God leads. He will not ask you to give up something you can't. God won't ask you to do something He wouldn't empower you to do. Where can you start?

3. Respond to God's provision — As God empowers you to trust Him, do it. Begin to work with God, not against Him. Get into His stride and run at His pace.

4. Receive God's promises — We draw strength from His promises.

He gives strength to the weary.
And to him who lacks might He increases power.
Though youths grow weary and tired, and vigorous young men stumble badly,
yet those who wait for the Lord will gain new strength;
they will mount up with wings like eagles,
they will run and not get tired,
they will walk and not become weary (Isaiah 40:29-31).

Delight yourself in the Lord;
and He will give you the desires of your heart.
Commit your way to the Lord,
Trust also in Him, and He will do it (Psalm 37:4-5).

"Come to Me, all who are weary and heavy-laden, and I will give you rest. Take My yoke upon you, and learn from Me, for I am gentle and humble in heart; and you shall find rest for your souls. For My yoke is easy, and My load is light" (Matthew 11:28-30).

I can do all things through Him who strengthens me (Philippians 4:13).

PRAY through these Scriptures for yourself. Receive the comfort and strength of God's promises to you.

Because we do not continually hand over our burdens to Christ, many of us are living far below our possibilities. The secret of the gospel is that you don't have to live life on your own. Galatians 2:20 says that it is no longer you, but Christ who lives in you! You aren't in the boat alone. Paul said in 1 Corinthians 15:10 that it was not him anymore, but the grace of God in him. Casting your burdens on God and letting Him work in you is a giant step of maturity.

QUENCHING
GOING THE EXTRA MILE
THE SPIRIT

2

So what does the Holy Spirit do? You have to know what to look for. You need to be sensitive to His leading. Let's look at Scripture for insight about the work of the Holy Spirit.

"And I will ask the Father, and He will give you another Helper, that He may be with you forever; that is the Spirit of truth, whom the world cannot receive, because it does not behold Him or know Him, but you know Him because He abides with you and will be in you" (John 14:16-17).

"The Helper, the Holy Spirit whom the Father will send in My name, He will teach you all things, and bring to your remembrance all that I said to you" (John 14:26).

Jhen Christ stepped out of heaven and into your heart, He placed the Holy Spirit inside of you. The Spirit acts as a guide and a guard. When we get a little too close to the edge, the Spirit of God sticks His arm out and says, "That's far enough." But, someone who doesn't get it will push the arm aside and say, "Don't tell me what to do. I can handle this."

"He, when He comes, will convict the world concerning sin, and righteousness, and judgment" (John 16:8).

"When He, the Spirit of truth, comes, He will guide you into all the truth; for He will not speak His own initiative, but whatever He hears, He will speak; and He will disclose to you what is to come. He shall glorify Me; for He shall take of Mine, and shall disclose it to you" (John 16:13-14).

The Spirit will be with us forever. See John 14:16.

The Spirit lives with us and in us. See John 14:17.

You cannot wander away from the presence of the Holy Spirit. He lives inside you. You can grow hard and insensitive, but you cannot be without Him.

The Spirit teaches us about spiritual things. See John 14:26.

Ever had a light bulb come on about Scripture? Something finally made sense? That's the Holy Spirit.

The Spirit reminds us of Jesus' words. See John 14:26.

Has there ever been a time when you surprised yourself by remembering a Scripture or line from a sermon? That was the Spirit of God reminding you of Jesus.

Has God been reminding you of a Scripture or thought? ❏ yes ❏ no If so, describe below.

. . . .

. . . .

The Spirit convicts us of sin. See John 16:8.

If you are reminded of unfinished business or forgiveness you need to seek, that's the Holy Spirit.

Is there any unconfessed sin that you need to deal with? ❏ yes ❏ no If so, write a prayer confessing that sin and ask God for His forgiveness.

. . . .

. . . .

The Spirit guides us into truth. See John 16:13.

You're in a situation that seems OK, but then you get a knot in your stomach. All of a sudden, you can't explain it, but you know something's not right. You decide to choose differently based on a "feeling." That's the Holy Spirit guiding you. When you really think about your life, is there an area you don't feel right about? ❏ yes ❏ no If so, describe below.

. . . .

The Spirit brings glory to Christ. See John 16:14.

When you make wise decisions, when others see Jesus in you, that's the Holy Spirit working through you to glorify Christ.

"Do not quench the Spirit" **(1Thessalonians 5:19).**

DAVE QUOTE

Quenching the Spirit means that you toss aside His leadership.

Read these passages in Ephesians and consider how you may be missing God's leadership.

"Laying aside falsehood, speak the truth, each one of you, with his neighbor, for we are members of one another. Be angry and yet do not sin; do not let the sun go down on your anger" (Ephesians 4:25-26).

We quench the Spirit by the way we speak, in anger or falsely.

How do you quench the Spirit of God with your speech?

. . . .

"Let all bitterness and wrath and anger and clamor and slander be put away from you, along with all malice. And be kind to one another, tenderhearted, forgiving each other, just

DAVE QUOTE

We're all born in the driver's seat — holding on to the steering wheel. When you accept Jesus as your Savior, it means you slide over and give Him the wheel. You quench the Spirit when you put your hand back on the wheel and try to help steer. Someone once said, "If you want to get along with God, stay out of the driver's seat."

as God in Christ also has forgiven you" (Ephesians 4:31-32).

We quench the Spirit by letting emotions rule our actions.

How should we choose to act?

. . . .

"Be imitators of God, as beloved children; and walk in love, just as Christ also loved you, and gave Himself up for us, an offering and a sacrifice to God as a fragrant aroma. But do not let immorality or any impurity or greed even be named among you, as is proper among saints" (Ephesians 5:1-3).

We quench the Spirit when we live by our instincts.

How should we live by God's principles?

. . . .

PRAY for a heart that is always ready to hear and respond to the Holy Spirit.

1. What principle or truth have you learned about the journey?

. . . .

. . . .

. . . .

. . . .

. . . .

2. What do you feel God is trying to say to you about your journey?

. . . .

. . . .

. . . .

. . . .

. . . .

3. What new steps can you take toward the destination (things to do, things to change, things to avoid)?

. . . .

. . . .

. . . .

VIEWING

SIGNS THAT YOU DON'T GET TWO PART I

Mark 8:14-21

¹⁴And they had forgotten to take bread; and did not have more than one loaf in the boat with them.

¹⁵And He was giving orders to them, saying, "Watch out! Beware of the leaven of the Pharisees and the leaven of Herod."

¹⁶And they began to discuss with one another the fact that they had no bread.

¹⁷And Jesus, aware of this, said to them, "Why do you discuss the fact that you have no bread? Do you not yet see or understand? Do you have a hardened heart?

¹⁸"Having eyes, do you not see? And having ears, do you not hear? And do you not remember,

¹⁹When I broke the five loaves for the five thousand, how many baskets full of broken pieces you picked up?" They said to Him, "Twelve."

²⁰"And when I broke the seven for the four thousand, how many large baskets full of broken pieces did you pick up?" And they said to Him, "Seven."

²¹And He said to them, "Do you not yet understand?"

GUIDE

2. People who don't get it initiate . . . .
   (Mark 8:17)

. . . .

Worry is . . . .

. . . .

Good news for people who don't get it: . . . .

. . . .

Jesus was trying to get the disciples to see that it wasn't the bread that fed them, it was . . . . . .

. . . .

He wants us to look at His face, not . . . .

. . . .

3. People who don't get it grow insensitive to . . . .
(Mark 8:17-18)

. . . .

God wants us to return . . . .

Discussion Questions

1. Describe your wildest worry.

2. When was the last time you really noticed the wonder of God?

3. Describe a time that God provided without you even asking.

STRUGGLING WITH WORRY
GOING THE EXTRA MILE

Having only one loaf of bread worried the disciples. They were anxious about where their next meal would come from. They worried about everything except the things that really mattered. They were missing the instruction of Jesus because they were consumed with their fears. They were missing out on all that God had to offer them because they were trying to solve their own problems.

God is offering total provision for your burdens and worries. He continues to lavish you with grace for each situation, whether you choose to receive it or not. Dottie Connor Bingham writes in her *Grace for the Rest of Your Life*: "Grace is like a moving sidewalk. The power of the sidewalk is a given. The question is what will we do with it." We can get on the sidewalk and refuse to put our burden down, resisting the total provision of the sidewalk. "[We can become] angry because it's not moving faster. [We can] experience the pain of resistance by hanging on to the siderails. [We can even] turn our backs and walk the other way, ... If we were to run this other way, we'd eventually fall exhausted and the grace would still be there carrying us along."[1]

God's solution for all your worries is "sufficient grace." He is faithful to see you through even the hardest days. God wants to carry you if you will allow Him. You can continue to try to carry your stuff all by yourself and refuse the grace that God continues to pour out for you.

Why do we resist God's grace and continue to worry?
1. Fear — of what we can't see.
2. Pride — we think we have all the answers, or we'll figure out what we don't know.
3. Desire to control.
4. Doubt God's ability — mistakenly act like we are serving a small God with limited power.

Can you think of other reasons you resist God?

. . . .

. . . .

Our job is to rest in God's grace. Psalm 55:22 says, "Cast your burden upon the Lord, and He will sustain you."

DAVE QUOTE

Worry is trying to solve your problems without the help of God. It's like having a map and not looking at it.

What is your job according to this Psalm?

. . . .

. . . .

> What I'm facing is temporary, but
> Who I'm trusting is timeless.

And He has said to me, "My grace is sufficient for you, for power is perfected in weakness" (2 Corinthians 12:9).

What is God's job?

. . . .

. . . .

"Blessed be the Lord, who daily bears our burden, the God who is our salvation" (Psalm 68:19).

Are you resting or resisting?

. . . .

"Casting all your anxiety upon Him, because He cares for you" (1 Peter 5:7).

To rest, we need the ...

1. Right perspective — I can't, but God can.
2. Right purpose — There is a reason for this. God has a reason. He wants me to look at Him and stop trying to get stuff from Him.
3. Right priority — You must consciously choose to give your worries to God. Allow the One who has more strength to carry the load.

At some point in your journey toward maturity, you have to start living what you say you believe. If you are growing, what you believe has to make a difference in how you react and respond. When do we stop pretending to trust Jesus, and truly begin to live like we do?

Take some time to PRAY through these Scriptures about resting in the grace of God.

"Rest in the Lord and wait patiently for Him" (Psalm 37:7).

The result of casting our burden on the Lord is that He will sustain our attitudes, emotions, and reactions. Stop resisting the grace of God and rest in His provision and promise.

MISSING THE WONDERS OF GOD

The disciples did not have eyes to see, ears to hear, or a mind to remember the wonders of God. Their world had caved in and they were missing the glory of God. We miss the wonders of God when we become preoccupied and insensitive. Have you worshiped the wonder of God lately? Are you looking for reasons to praise the Lord?

Let's worship Him, guided by the experience of the prophet Isaiah.

1. Confrontation of the Spirit

In the year of King Uzziah's death, I saw the Lord sitting on a throne, lofty and exalted, with the train of His robe filling the temple. Seraphim stood above Him, each having six wings; with two he covered his face, and with two he covered his feet, and with two he flew. And one called out to another and said,

"Holy, Holy, Holy, is the Lord of hosts,
the whole earth is full of His glory."

And the foundations of the thresholds trembled at the voice of him who called out, while the temple was filling with smoke (Isaiah 6.1-4).

Isaiah met God. In true worship we are to meet the spirit of God. It's the difference between singing a few choruses, or praying a few lines and then stopping, or continuing until God shows up.

Take some time now to meet with God. Sing, pray, or meditate on Him. You'll know that you are beginning to worship when your heart and mind are full of thoughts about Him.

2. Confession of Self

Then I said,
"Woe is me, for I am ruined!
Because I am a man of unclean lips
And I live among a people of unclean lips;
For my eyes have seen the King, the Lord of hosts" (Isaiah 6:5).

Isaiah realized he was unclean before God. When we worship, the condition of our heart becomes obvious. You become aware of who you really are. You can't hide. You can't play games. Confession is mandatory. The hard part of confession is being honest about the sin we've tried to hide. The gift of confession is that it brings peace and refreshment.

Spend some time with God in confession. Let the light of His presence shine on the dark places.

3. Cleansing of Sin

Then one of the seraphim flew to me, with a burning coal in his hand which he had taken from the altar with tongs. And he touched my mouth with it and said, "Behold, this has touched your lips; and your iniquity is taken away, and your sin is forgiven" (Isaiah 6:6-7).

The angel of the Lord removed Isaiah's confessed sin.

If we confess our sins, He is faithful and righteous to forgive us our sins and to cleanse us from all unrighteousness (1 John 1:9).

Thank God for His ability and willingness to cleanse you from sin. He is faithful to cast it into the depths of the sea and remember it no more.

4. Call to Serve

Then I heard the voice of the Lord, saying, "Whom shall I send, and who will go for Us?" Then I said, "Here am I. Send me!" (Isaiah 6: 8).

Then, after a time of worship, Isaiah was sent out by God for service. The result of true worship is that we should be able to hear God speak to us. We can't short-circuit the process and step ahead. One of the things Isaiah heard was what God wanted him to do with his life.

Listen as God speaks to you in this time of worship. How God leads and what He talks to you about is up to Him.

How has God spoken to you as you worshiped Him? Record your thoughts here.

. . . .

. . . .

. . . .

The heavens will praise Thy wonders, O Lord;
Thy faithfulness also in the assembly of the holy ones (Psalm 89:5).

I trust in the lovingkindness of God forever and ever.
I will give Thee thanks forever, because Thou hast done it,
And I will wait on Thy name, for it is good, in the presence of Thy godly ones (Psalm 52:8-9).

THERE IS HOPE

GOING THE EXTRA MILE

2

The good news is that God is sovereign and patient with those who don't get it. When the disciples began to worry and fear, Jesus could have gotten out of the boat and walked away. He could have thrown up His hands in frustration and yelled, "Forget this, I'm tired of you guys," but He didn't. He loved His men through their blindness and fears. There is hope for all the Pharisees and doubting disciples.

Along the journey, when we have made wrong turns and taken side roads, we begin to feel abandoned, without value, and useless. We become fertile soil for Satan. BUT, God doesn't see us that way. We are still His beloved, His chosen, the object of His love and affection.

We have hope because:
We are God's treasured creation—loved before we ever were.
We have a salvation that is secure.
We have a home in heaven.
God would do anything to reclaim His own.
God is patient with our shortcomings.
Jesus went to the cross, and the tomb was empty.

What earthly things have you put your hope in?

. . . .

Look at these passages to find out where you should put your hope.

This hope we have as an anchor of the soul, a hope, both sure and steadfast and one which enters within the veil (Hebrews 6:19).

For it is for this we labor and strive, because we have fixed our hope on the living God, who is the Savior of all men, especially of believers (1 Timothy 4:10).

My soul, wait in silence for God only, for my hope is from Him.
He only is my rock and my salvation, my stronghold; I shall not be shaken.
On God my salvation and my glory rest;
The rock of my strength, my refuge is in God.
Trust in Him at all times, O people;
Pour out your heart before Him;
God is a refuge for us (Psalm 62:5-8).

"For I know the plans that I have for you," declares the Lord, "plans for welfare and not for calamity to give you a future and a hope" (Jeremiah 29:11).

From these verses, where is our hope secure?

. . . .

Even if you lost your way for awhile, there is always hope. If you look up from the journey and all you can see is wilderness, then turn in the direction of Calvary and let the light of God's love guide you back. Cry out to Him in your defeat and stop fumbling to find your way in the dark. The hope of Christ can lift you up, turn you around, and refocus your eyes on the destination.

Ephesians 5:1-21 gives us some good advice about returning to the main road. Read these verses below:

Get your heart and mind back on the destination. Be imitators of God and walk in the love of Christ.

Be imitators of God, as beloved children; and walk in love, just as Christ also loved you and gave Himself up for us, an offering and a sacrifice to God as a fragrant aroma (Ephesians 5:1-2).

Get good directions. Let no one deceive you. Instead, obey the instructions given to those who believe in Jesus. Surround yourself with others who are like-minded. Find a church where they preach from the Bible and lavish the grace of Christ. Get with other godly people who can help you read the map. Do not let immorality or any impurity or greed even be named among you, as is proper among saints; and there must be no filthiness and silly talk, or coarse jesting, which are not fitting, but rather giving of thanks. For this you know with certainty, that no immoral or impure person or covetous man, who is an idolater, has an inheritance in the kingdom of Christ and God. Let no one deceive you with empty words, for because of these things the wrath of God comes upon the sons of disobedience (Ephesians 5:3-6).

Go. Do not participate in unfruitful deeds. You may have to physically remove yourself from the wrong road. Whatever it takes, get away from wrong choices.

Do not be partakers with them; for you were formerly darkness, but now you are light in the Lord; walk as children of light (for the fruit of the light consists in all goodness and righteousness and truth), trying to learn what is pleasing to the Lord. And do not participate in the unfruitful deeds of darkness, but instead even expose them; for it is disgraceful even to speak of the things which are done by them in secret. But all things become visible when they are exposed by the light, for everything that becomes visible is light.
> For this reason it says,
> "Awake sleeper,
> And arise from the dead,
> And Christ will shine on you."
> Therefore be careful how you walk, not as unwise men, but as wise, making the most of your time, because the days are evil (Ephesians 5:7-16).

DIRECTIONS FOR RETURNING TO THE MAIN ROAD

1. Start defensively. Be careful; guard what He's already done in you up to this point.
2. Seek direction. Stay in God's Word.
3. Shun distractions. Do not be easily entangled with your old sin habits or the sin of others.
4. Surrender daily. Start each day fresh with God.
5. Spiritually develop. Don't be satisfied to stay where you are. Continue to grow up in Jesus.

Maybe you have noticed some signs that you're off the main road. Maybe you've decided that you're just totally lost. Whatever the case, there's no need to be afraid. Your Father is the Good Shepherd who will do whatever it takes to find and restore even the one who is lost. God created the world from nothing. He can surely remake our lives when we come to Him empty and without resources. The solution for the wayward disciple is to claim desperate dependence on the Savior.

PRAY for the Lord to find you in your helplessness. Thank God for being the Hope that is secure. Thank God for His faithfulness to you even when you lost your way. Commit your way to Him anew, and receive His cleansing and restoration.

"Redemption/Restoration is that activity of the grace of God that not only forgives a man's sins, but also restores and overrules all the loss occasioned by his sin. ... We make mistakes and wrong choices because of self-will, and can find ourselves in grievous and complicated situations as a result. But failure with God is never final. Jesus Christ is the Redeemer of lost men and lost situations, whether the situation has been wrong for half a lifetime, or only a day. And when He moves in to redeem/restore, He not only forgives the sin we confess, but He also overrules for good the whole situation in which we have landed ourselves. And when He starts doing that sort of thing, He does it in style. He so often gives back to a man far more than he forfeited, so that he cannot go on blaming himself, but is lost in wonder, love, and praise for all that grace has done for a poor failure like himself. Oh, this great and marvellous God of redemption/restoration!"[2]

———

1Dottie Connor Bingham, Grace for the Rest of Your Life (Englewood, Col.: Gracestoration, 1990)

2Roy Hession, Our Nearest Kinsman: The Message of Redemption and Revival in the Book of Ruth (Fort Washington, Penn.: Christian Literature Crusade, 1976).

1. What principle or truth have you learned about the journey?

· ·

· ·

· ·

· ·

· ·

2. What do you feel God is trying to say to you about your journey?

· ·

· ·

· ·

· ·

· ·

3. What new steps can you take toward the destination (things to do, things to change, things to avoid)?

· ·

· ·

· ·

Enjoy the Ride

ENJOY
OTHE
RIDE

3

"I HAVE DIRECTED YOU IN
THE WAY
OF WISDOM;
I HAVE LED YOU IN
UPRIGHT PATHS.

/PROVERBS 4:10:15/.

In the book of Proverbs, those who made wise choices were rewarded with blessings, and poor choices were followed by consequences. Deciding to live by God's instruction makes you a person of principle. You believe that God is who He says He is, that the Bible is true, and that He guides you through His Word. Through obedience to His principles, you begin to mature spiritually and look more like Jesus. The first steps of obedience begin a maturing cycle that continues all throughout your journey. Obedience results in wise choices, wise choices make application of Scripture, and application produces greater maturity.

In Proverbs 3, we're going to look at the rewards attached to choosing the path of wisdom. The secret of the Christian life is trusting God with the details. Every time we choose to trust God with a detail, we reap godly results. When we apply the principles of Proverbs, then we make a way to receive the promises of God. The ride is a lot easier when we make wise choices. We enjoy it so much more when the consequences of immaturity aren't knocking us around.

How do you want to get to the destination? You can still get there in a dumpy car that barely runs. If you take a lot of wrong turns, you'll still arrive, but the trip will be frustrating. You'll miss all the things you were supposed to do along the way. Without maintenance you could be stuck on the side of the road and may even have to walk part of the way. Wouldn't you rather enjoy the ride? Then read the map. Be kind to strangers along the way. Ask for directions when you're lost. Pace yourself for the journey with regular maintenance and tune-ups. Believe in the destination, even when you can't see it. Most of all, never forget the One who planned the trip. He knows what the next stop is. He has made reservations for you. He is an awesome travel guide.

Wisdom is so valuable that we should run after it and pray for it. It guards us from the wicked and keeps us choosing right paths for the journey. Wise choices ensure that we enjoy the ride.

VIEWING

ENJOY THE RIDE PART ONE

Proverbs 3:1-4

[1]My son, do not forget my teaching,
But let your heart keep my commandments;
[2]For length of days and years of life,
And peace they will add to you.
[3]Do not let kindness and truth leave you;
Bind them around your neck,
Write them on the tablet of your heart.
[4]So you will find favor and good repute
In the sight of God and man.

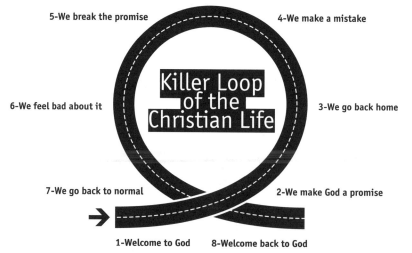

Killer Loop of the Christian Life

5-We break the promise

4-We make a mistake

6-We feel bad about it

3-We go back home

7-We go back to normal

2-We make God a promise

1-Welcome to God

8-Welcome back to God

GUIDE

The secret of the Christian life is: . . . .

. . . .

Every time I choose to trust God with the details of my life: . . . .

. . . .

The Reasons for Trusting God with the Details
(Proverbs 3)

Verse 1 - demand - Do not forget my . . . .
Verse 2 - positive result - So . . . . will be added to you.

Reason #1: . . . .

Verse 3 - demand - Do not let . . . . and . . . . leave you.

Verse 4 - positive result - so you will find favor and success in the sight of. . . . . and . . . .

Reason #2: . . . .
(Enjoy the Ride Viewing Guide continues on page 63.)

Discussion Questions

1. What does a "peaceless" life look like? feel like? How do we lose our peace?
2. Name every area you can think of where truth is a rare commodity. Has pretending replaced truth in the majority of our relationships?

54

DO NOT FORGET
PRINCIPLE NUMBER ONE
GOD'S TEACHING

Proverbs 3:1-12 contains six principles accompanied by six promises. The overriding principle in Proverbs 3 is that every time you choose to trust God with the details, you reap God-like results.

My son, do not forget my teaching; But let your heart keep my commandments (Proverbs 3:1).

There is the story of a youth pastor who took his senior-high group on a mission trip to Florida. Before they left, he built a cross from railroad ties, put some wheels on it, and made someone responsible for the cross every minute. The cross had to go with the youth group everywhere. If they went into a restaurant, the cross went, too. If they were on the beach, a student drug it out and propped it in the sand. The cross became the focus of their week. It was a constant reminder of their purpose. The cross became the core of who they were. At the end of the week, the pastor gave each student two nails. One to nail in the cross if

A recent study found that 85 percent of the people polled say the Bible has no part in their daily lives. You know what that tells me? That many of us live making decisions by whatever seems best at the moment. We are doing whatever seems right. Whatever needs to happen, that's what we do instead of being principle-oriented and acting based on what the Word of God says. We aren't acting based on God's teaching.

DAVEQUOTE

DAVE QUOTE

God says, "When you take my words, place them into your life, and keep my commandments, then peace will be added to you." God puts the restriction about His teaching on your life, not because He hates you, not because He is more like your parents than like you, not because He is trying to even up the score because you've been a bad person, but because God is trying to get His peace into your life so you can be all you are created to be.

they had determined that Jesus, and the cross, would be the focus of their lives, and one to keep as a reminder. You can bet those students never forgot that trip or hauling that cross around. They also remember the lesson of keeping Christ as the focus of all they do.

Proverbs 3:1 says that we should never forget God's teachings. We should keep our hearts focused on His Word. Essentially, we must keep God's instruction at the core of who we are. The cross of Christ must be the focus of our hearts.

What is at the core of who you are?

. . . .

What kinds of things compete for your core?

. . . .

Take a look at some practical ways to keep God's teaching at your core:

1. Hear God's Word

"So faith comes from hearing, and hearing by the word of Christ" (Romans 10:17).

What are the ways you hear God's Word?

. . . .

. . . .

2. Read God's Word

As you read the Bible, ask yourself, "What is God saying through this passage?" and "What is God saying to me?"

"Blessed is he who reads and those who hear the words of the prophecy, and heed the things which are written in it; for the time is near" (Revelation 1:3).

Do you read God's Word?
❑ yes ❑ no How often? In what forms?

. . . .

3. Study God's Word

"Now these were more noble-minded than those in Thessalonica, for they received the word with great eagerness, examining the Scriptures daily, to see whether these things were so" (Acts 17:11).

How do you study God's Word?

. . . .

4. Memorize God's Word

"Thy word I have treasured in my heart,
That I may not sin against Thee" (Psalm 119:11).

How does it help you when you memorize God's Word?

. . . .

5. Meditate on God's Word

"His delight is in the law of the Lord,
And in His law he meditates day and night.
And he will be like a tree firmly planted by streams of water,
Which yields its fruit in its season,
And its leaf does not wither;
And in whatever he does, he prospers" (Psalm 1:2-3).

How do you meditate on God's Word?

. . . .

. . . .

For length of days and years of life, And peace they will add to you (Proverbs 3:2).

PROMISE #1: You get the peace of God in your life.

The promise for remembering God's teaching is peace. Peace in your life means that you are untroubled by conflict, agitation, or commotion. The world may be caving in around you, circumstances may be chaotic; but on the inside, because of a supernatural work of God, you are calm and peaceful. Trusting God with the details by remembering God's teaching produces a confident assurance.

In what situation are you least peaceful?

. . . .

Look at these Scriptures.
Christ is speaking: " 'Peace I leave with you; My peace I give to you; not as the world gives, do I give to you. Let not your heart be troubled, nor let it be fearful' " (John 14:27).

So, who is the giver of peace?

. . . .

"But the fruit of the Spirit is love, joy, peace, patience, kindness, goodness, faithfulness, gentleness, self-control; against such things there is no law" (Galatians 5:22).

We don't have to figure out how to get the peace. It is produced by the power of the Holy Spirit, working through a Christian who is in a vital relationship with Christ. When we remember God's teachings and apply them, then one of the "fruit" of our obedience is peace. What is peace for you? Describe a peaceful time. A peaceful life.

. . . .

. . . .

"And the peace of God, which surpasses all comprehension, shall guard your hearts and your minds in Christ Jesus" (Philippians 4:7).

Jessica was a friend who had dedicated her life to the Lord. She even went through her home and gave each room to God. When her husband prospered, they moved into a huge estate. Again she went through the house and gave each room to the Lord. She prayed for her family and asked the Lord that they would not become attached to their beautiful home and the things they had. A few years later, she walked down their long drive to get the mail. When she looked back, she could see that the house was on fire. She said that the run back to her house was the greatest lesson of her life. She knew right then that God had answered her prayers. Her house was burning before her eyes and she really wasn't attached to it. She had a peace she didn't even understand. She knew it was a gift from God.

Peace beyond understanding, in the midst of circumstances, is God's assurance that everything is OK.

Have you ever experienced peace that was beyond your understanding?

. . . .

How would peace improve the quality of your life?

. . . .

. . . .

. . . .

. . . .

PRAY for a heart that is faithful to the teachings of God.

DO NOT LET

KINDNESS AND TRUTH LEAVE YOU

Do not let kindness and truth leave you;
Bind them around your neck,
Write them on the tablet of your heart (Proverbs 3:3).

Character is a huge issue. Ultimately every relationship succeeds or fails based on character. The things that we most want to change about people in our lives are character-related issues. We expect character from everyone we deal with, but it's something we don't often develop on our own. There are no conditions attached to verse 3. It doesn't say to have kindness and truth if it benefits you, or if it makes you happy, but to always have it—to not ever let it leave you. Let all of your relationships be built on godly character, beginning with kindness and truth. We must choose to be godly in spite of, or no matter how we're treated. Think about how you drive. Sometimes who we really are comes out in traffic. How do you act behind the wheel? We get behind the wheel then yell, scream, and shake our fists. We talk to people like they can

hear us through the glass. We race to empty parking spots, cut people off, follow too closely, and that's all just trying to get out of the church parking lot. The point is, we have to choose godly character, under pressure, in secret, and even in traffic.

In Psalm 15, David provides some guidelines for living a blameless life.

^{1}O Lord, who may abide in Thy tent?
Who may dwell on Thy holy hill?
^{2}He who walks with integrity, and works righteousness,
And speaks truth in his heart.
^{3}He does not slander with his tongue,
Nor does evil to his neighbor,
Nor takes up a reproach against his friend;
^{4}In whose eyes a reprobate is despised,
But who honors those who fear the Lord;
He swears to his own hurt, and does not change;
^{5}He does not put out his money at interest,
Nor does he take a bribe against the innocent.
He who does these things will never be shaken.

Go back and underline the things in Psalm 15 that describe a person of character. How would you live them out?

. . . .

. . . .

. . . .

In verse 5, there is a promise. Go back and circle the promise. How would godly character keep your life from being shaken?

. . . .

. . . .

DAVE QUOTE

You get into a relationship with someone, and it's supposed to be built on kindness and truth. But what do most of us do? We meet someone we want to get to know; so for about the first four or five weeks, we go out with them and act like somebody else. I don't know what it is, but we get in a relationship, and have to pretend we're something we're not so they can get to know us. What's that about? Where's the kindness and truth in that?

So you will find favor and good repute
In the sight of God and man (Proverbs 3:4).

PROMISE #2: You can have a successful relationship with God and others.
When you build relationships based on character, you get to miss out on the heartache that comes from pretending and deceit.

With character as a priority, write a want ad for a successful relationship.

CLASSIFIED

Guys and girls get out of long-term relationships and say something like, "We dated for five years, and I've got nothing to show for it." I say, you better have character to show for it.

Top 10 Signs That It's Time to Dump the Guy
10. He responds to your requests with, "Yes ma'am!"
 9. When you mention commitment, he starts shaking uncontrollably.
 8. He demands that all your future communications be done through Email.
 7. He writes down everything you say.
 6. His name is Jack but insists that you call him Jacque.
 5. He offers you a cigar.
 4. He doesn't leave a tip at restaurants because "those waiters make way too much money."
 3. He asks, "Have you ever thought about wearing your hair differently?"
 2. He uses one of those pens that can write in four different colors.

And the number one sign that it's time to dump the guy …
 1. He offers to hypnotize you.

PRAY for the character of Christ in all you do, and for successful relationships with God and man.

TRUST IN GOD AND LEAN NOT
PRINCIPLE NUMBER THREE
ON YOUR OWN UNDERSTANDING

Trust in the Lord with all your heart, and do not lean on your own understanding.
In all your ways acknowledge Him, And He will make your paths straight (Proverbs 3:5-6).

PROMISE #3: You can know and experience God's will.

Along the road, there are helps and protectors to keep you safe and on the path—guard rails, speed bumps, traffic lights, road signs, and the occasional intervention of a police officer. The wise traveler heeds the signs and takes instruction well. Knowing the will of God for your life starts with heeding the instructions that have already been given.

Road Rules

Here are three instructions from Scripture that involve the phrase, "It is the will of God." When faced with questions about these areas, you don't have to ask, "Is it God's will?" You can know for sure that God wants you to apply the teaching in these passages.

1. That You Would Know Him Personally

"This is good and acceptable in the sight of God our Savior, who desires all men to be saved and to come to the knowledge of the truth" (1 Timothy 2:3-4).

Through a relationship with Him, you begin to see yourself as God really sees you—completely changed, totally forgiven, and eternally loved.

Are you confident that you know Him personally? ❑ yes ❑ no Why?

. . . .

. . . .

2. That You Would Imitate God

Therefore be imitators of God, as beloved children; and walk in love, just as Christ also loved you, and gave Himself up for us, an offering and a sacrifice to God as a fragrant aroma. But do not let immorality or any impurity or greed even be named among you, as is proper among saints; and there must be no filthiness and silly talk, or coarse jesting, which are not fitting, but rather giving of thanks. For this you know with certainty, that no immoral or impure person or covetous man, who is an idolater, has an inheritance in the kingdom of Christ and God. Let no one deceive you with empty words, for because of these things the wrath of God comes upon the sons of disobedience. Therefore do not be partakers with them; for you were formerly darkness, but now you are light in the Lord; walk as children of light (for the fruit of the light consists in all goodness and righteousness and truth), trying to learn what is pleasing to the Lord. So then do not be foolish, but understand what the will of the Lord is (Ephesians 5:1-10,17).

DAVE
QUOTE

A friend of mine once told me that the will of God is not a tightwire; it's a canyon. It's not something you slip off of, it's something you walk around in.

Imitating God means that you begin to love the things He loves, hate the things He hates, feel compassion where He would feel compassion, talk the way He would talk, and sacrifice where He would sacrifice.

Are you interested in what God is interested in, or do you just go to God to get something?

. . . .

Where do you look most like God? Where do you look least like God?

. . . .

. . . .

3. That You Would Do What Is Right No Matter What the Circumstance
"For such is the will of God that by doing right you may silence the ignorance of foolish men" (1 Peter 2:15).

"If you are reviled for the name of Christ, you are blessed, because the Spirit of glory and of God rests upon you. By no means let any of you suffer as a murderer, or thief, or evildoer, or a troublesome meddler; but if anyone suffers as a Christian, let him not feel ashamed, but in that name

let him glorify God. Therefore, let those also who suffer according to the will of God entrust their souls to a faithful Creator in doing what is right" (1 Peter 4:14-16,19).

We can know for sure that it is always the will of God for us to do right. Sometimes we choose rightly and still suffer. First Peter 4:16 says that if you suffer for being a Christian, don't be ashamed, but glorify God. When you do God's will, the results aren't always immediately positive. Sometimes you take heat for doing the right thing.

Have you ever suffered for choosing to honor Christ? ❏ yes ❏ no How?

. . . .

. . . .

If you are applying the above principles—the Road Rules, then the only question you have to ask is, "What do I want to do?" If you're living in these, then your desires will be His desires, and your dreams will be His dreams.

How Can I Be Sure It's God's Will?
1. Pay attention to your desires. God places desires and dreams in us to fulfill us, not to frustrate us. God wouldn't create you to do something you don't want to do.

2. Get confirmation from God's Word. Does what you desire go against His Word or conflict with God's character? If it does, then you can be sure it's not His will. As you read the Word, look for the promises that confirm or deny your desires.

3. Get godly counsel. You should have people in your life that know more about God than you do, who have walked with God longer, and who can be trustworthy advisors.

PRAY for a trusting heart that you might know the will of God.

DAVE QUOTE

Who's ruling your wants? Are God's desires becoming your desires? Or are you just trying to use Him to get your own way?

1. What principle or truth have you learned about the journey?

. . . .

. . . .

. . . .

. . . .

. . . .

2. What do you feel God is trying to say to you about your journey?

. . . .

. . . .

. . . .

. . . .

. . . .

3. What new steps can you take toward the destination (things to do, things to change, things to avoid)?

. . . .

. . . .

. . . .

VIEWING

ENJOY THE RIDE

PART TWO

Proverbs 3:5-12

[5]Trust in the Lord with all your heart,
And do not lean on your own understanding.
[6]In all your ways acknowledge Him,
And He will make your paths straight.
[7]Do not be wise in your own eyes;
Fear the Lord and turn away from evil.
[8]It will be healing to your body,
And refreshment to your bones.
[9]Honor the Lord from your wealth,
And from the first of all your produce;
[10]So your barns will be filled with plenty,
And your vats will overflow with new wine.
[11]My son, do not reject the discipline of the Lord,
Or loathe His reproof,
[12]For whom the Lord loves He reproves,
Even as a father, the son in whom he delights.

GUIDE

Verse 5 - demand -. . . . . in the Lord with all your heart.

Do not lean on your own . . . .

Verse 6 - positive result - And He will make your path . . . .

Reason #3: . . . .

. . . .

Verse 7 - demand - Do not . . . .

Verse 8 - positive result - It will be . . . .

Reason #4:. . . . .

. . . .

Verse 11 - demand - Do not reject . . . .

Verse 12 - positive result - For whom the Lord loves, ...

Reason #5:. . . . .

. . . .

1. Are you making excuses for an area that is keeping you from reaching your full potential?

2. What's God pointing at in your life? Are you willing to hand it over to Him?

Discussion Questions

DO NOT BE WISE IN YOUR
PRINCIPLE NUMBER FOUR
OWN EYES, AND FEAR THE LORD

Proverbs 3 continues in the same direction, a principle followed by a promise. The writer calls us to choose the path of wisdom in all areas of our lives.

Do not be wise in your own eyes;
Fear the Lord and turn away from evil (Proverbs 3:7).

To be wise in your own eyes is to be self-centered and haughty toward others. Christians who don't fear God play games with God. Look at the following chart for some ways to know if you've become "wise in your own eyes."

Do any of these errors apply to where you are? ❑ yes ❑ no
Have you heard yourself using any of these excuses? ❑ yes ❑ no
Explain.

. . . .

. . . .

The Error	The Excuse
You justify sin.	It's just the way I am.
You ignore instruction and advise.	No one understands. It's different for me.
You mock your parents.	Things have changed. They don't understand my world.
You blame your failure on God.	I did my part, but God didn't do His. It's not my fault.
You repeat your mistakes.	Why does this always happen to me?
You trust in yourself.	I can work it out.
Your kindness has ulterior motives.	I just turn on the charm to get what I want.
You make fun of those with integrity.	They can't really be like that. It's gotta be an act.
When life is hard, you cave in.	Nobody could get through this.

Have you ever considered that justifying your sin is to become "wise in your own eyes"? Justifying your sin means that you value your wisdom over God's. Write a prayer of repentance for the times you have chosen your way over God's.

. . . .

. . . .

. . . .

. . . .

It will be healing to your body,
And refreshment to your bones
(Proverbs 3:8).

PROMISE #4: You can be spiritually and physically healthy.

If you fear the Lord and pursue righteousness, then you don't have to make excuses. There is spiritual health and favor in reverence toward God.

What are the options? You get to choose. You can choose to go through life fearing God and be assured of the outcome, or you can try it without God and hope for the best.

PRAY your prayer of repentance out loud to the Father.

HONOR THE LORD
PRINCIPLE NUMBER FIVE
WITH YOUR WEALTH

Honor the Lord from your wealth,
And from the first of all your produce
(Proverbs 3:9).

Giving to God from the first of our produce means that we give to Him from the top, from the first and best of our wealth. A lot of people give God what they have left over. They may mean well, but that idea is opposite of the instruction in verse 9. When we give God the first part of our income, we demonstrate that:

1. God has first place in our lives.
2. Everything we have belongs to God; we are only the managers.
3. Possessions don't have a hold on our lives.
4. We are more concerned about giving than greed.

When we manage God's money properly, we open ourselves up to receive God's blessings.

Let's look at some of the other teachings in Proverbs about money.

"There is one who scatters, yet increases all the more,
And there is one who withholds what is justly due, but it results only in want.
The generous man will be prosperous,
And he who waters will himself be watered" (Proverbs 11:24-25).

What is the principle of giving from this passage? How does it apply to you right now?

. . . .

. . . .

"A man lacking in sense pledges, and becomes surety in the presence of his neighbor" (Proverbs 17:18).

What are the dangers of cosigning for another person? Why would the Bible warn against it?

. . . .

. . . .

"A wicked man receives a bribe from the bosom
To pervert the ways of justice" (Proverbs 17:23).

How could accepting a bribe "come back to haunt you"?

. . . .

. . . .

"He who is gracious to a poor man lends to the Lord, and He will repay him for his good deed" (Proverbs 19:17).

DAVE QUOTE

What does your checkbook say about what you believe about God and money? If someone were to look through your entries and receipts, what would they think you believe about God by the way you spend your money?

God is identifying with the poor just like Jesus did. God says that if you give to the poor, it is as if you are giving to Him. What other things, in addition to money, can you provide for the poor?

. . . .

. . . .

There is precious treasure and oil in the dwelling of the wise,
But a foolish man swallows it up (Proverbs 21:20).

Have you been faithful to store up for the future, or do you think you're too young? This proverb says that the wise (no matter their age) will save for the future, and the foolish will use up everything they get. Have you been saving? ❑ yes ❑ no If yes, how could you improve? If no, what do you need to do to begin?

. . . .

. . . .

"The rich rules over the poor,
And the borrower becomes the lender's slave" (Proverbs 22:7).

If the borrower becomes slave to the lender, then what does this passage say about debt? If you have already become a slave to the lender, do you have a plan to get out of debt?
❑ yes ❑ no

What is your plan?

. . . .

. . . .

So your barns will be filled with plenty,
And your vats will overflow with new wine (Proverbs 3:10).

PROMISE #5: You can have your material needs supplied.

What you do with your money is a sign of maturity. It will be virtually impossible to reach the potential God has for you if you are continually spending more than you make, forever trapped under a pile of debt.

If you have already developed some unwise habits with money, the following could be helpful for you. In his book *Financial Peace*, Dave Ramsey outlines some steps to follow when you're overwhelmed by the financial mistakes you've made.

1. Pay minimum on everything you owe until you get $1000 in savings. Go crazy and get this emergency fund in place as soon as possible.

2. Kill all the debt. List your debts smallest to largest. Pay the smallest one off first and keep working up from there.

3. When you have no other debt than a home, then go back to your emergency fund and build it to three to six times your monthly expenses.

4. Fully fund all pretax retirement savings you possible can (for any age).

5. Pay the house off or begin saving for one.

6. With no debt left, begin building your wealth through real estate and mutual funds.[1]

DO NOT REJECT
PRINCIPLE NUMBER SIX
THE DISCIPLINE OF GOD

3

My son, do not reject the discipline of the Lord, or loathe His reproof (Proverbs 3:11).

For whom the Lord loves He reproves Even as a father, the son in whom he delights (Proverbs 3:12).

PROMISE #6: You will be fine-tuned by the love of God.

Discipline means "to teach and to train." God does not discipline us because He enjoys inflicting pain, but because He is concerned about the development of our character. He knows that to become morally strong and mature, we have to learn the difference between right and wrong. God's discipline helps us to do that. Let's look at another great passage about discipline from Hebrews 12.

> [5]You have forgotten the exhortation which is addressed to you as sons, "My son, do not regard lightly the discipline of the Lord, nor faint when you are reproved by him;
> [6]For those whom the Lord loves He disciplines, and He scourges every son whom He receives."
> [7]It is for discipline that you endure; God deals with you as with sons; for what son is there whom his father does not discipline?
> [8]But if you are without discipline, of which all have become partakers, then you are illegitimate children and not sons.
> [9]Furthermore, we had earthly fathers to discipline us, and we respected them; shall we not much rather be subject to the Father of spirits, and live?
> [10]For they disciplined us for a short time as seemed best to them, but He disciplines us for our good, that we may share His holiness.
> [11]All discipline for the moment seems not to be joyful, but sorrowful; yet to those who have been trained by it, afterwards it yields the peaceful fruit of righteousness.

According to this passage, why does the Father discipline?

. . . .

. . . .

What does verse 10 say is the result of our discipline?

. . . .

. . . .

DAVE QUOTE

Discipline is not God beating you and sending you to your room without dinner. Rather, God is refining those He loves, to be used for His glory.

There are several ways that we can respond to discipline.
1. We can accept it because it's inevitable.
2. We can think we don't really deserve it.
3. We can be angry and resentful.
4. We can accept it gratefully.

DAVE QUOTE

You can't do whatever you want and think it won't cost you something. The reason we get in trouble is that we think we can do anything without paying the consequences.

Can you think of a recent situation that may have been difficult, but was refining? ❏ yes ❏ no If so, describe it briefly below.

. . . .

. . . .

. . . .

How do you accept the discipline of your loving Father? Underline your answer from the list on the previous page or write it below.

. . . .

. . . .

DAVE QUOTE

Think back over your life and the price you've paid for carelessness. God intervenes and disciplines us to keep us from paying a higher price. God intervenes because He knows where we're gonna end up. God sees tomorrow like we see yesterday.

Revelation 3:19 says, " 'Those whom I love, I reprove and discipline; be zealous therefore, and repent.' " In this verse, God is disciplining a lukewarm church. They had become indifferent toward Him. Are you lukewarm in your relationship with God? God may discipline you to get your attention. The way to avoid God's discipline is to repent and return to fellowship with Him.

Think for a while about a refiner's pot. Mined gold is put into the pot. Fire is added to increase the heat. The heat separates the impurities from the gold. The impurities rise to the top and are scooped off and thrown away. Everything that remains is pure gold. The refiners pot can also represent each of our lives. Zechariah 13:9 says that " 'I will ... refine them as silver is refined, and test them as gold is tested.' " Our character is being forged in the refiner's pot. Through difficulty, disappointment, pain, sorrow, and discipline, the Lord brings our impurities to the top and scoops them off.

PRAY for a tender heart that longs to please God and accept His discipline. Praise God for the fires that have refined your life. Thank the Lord for loving you so much.

1Dave Ramsey, Financial Peace (Nashville, Tenn.: Lampo Press, 1992, 1995), 205-209.

DAVE QUOTE

Discipline is not always a bad thing. It's like the expression "fine-tuning a Cadillac." It's a great car, but it needs some fine-tuning.

1. What principle or truth have you learned about the journey?

. . . .

. . . .

. . . .

. . . .

. . . .

2. What do you feel God is trying to say to you about your journey?

. . . .

. . . .

. . . .

. . . .

. . . .

3. What new steps can you take toward the destination (things to do, things to change, things to avoid)?

. . . .

. . . .

. . . .

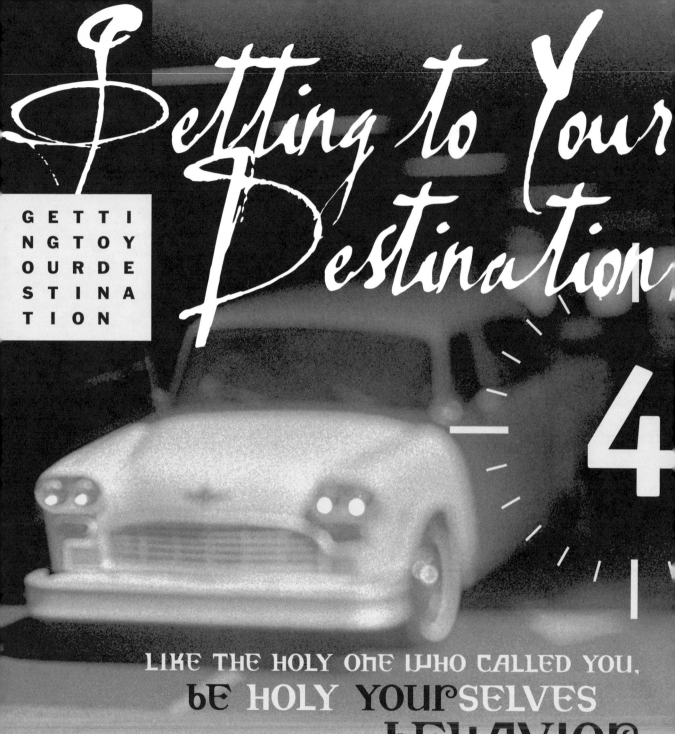

Getting to Your Destination

GETTING TO YOUR DESTINATION

4

LIKE THE HOLY ONE WHO CALLED YOU,
bE HOLY YOURSELVES
ALSO IN ALL YOUR **bEHAVIOR**;
bECAUSE IT IS WRITTEN, "YOU SHALL bE HOLY
FOR I AM HOLY" (1 PETER 1:14-16).

We begin the journey of maturity when Jesus moves into our lives. At the moment of salvation, believers are invaded by the very presence of God. Because of His presence, our purposes begin to change and come into focus. Our lives can't just be about us anymore, they have to be about the will of God through us.

God's presence in our lives is a call to holiness. Becoming holy means we start making decisions based on how they affect the Spirit of God inside us. The question "Is it holy?" is like a guard rail that keeps us from swerving off the edge of the road. Continually asking the question keeps us on the road toward maturity. There are many things that will distract us, but the call from the Bible is to flee anything that hinders holiness. The pursuit of holiness will keep us safely on the road—getting us to the destination.

VIEWING

GETTING TO YOUR DESTINATION PART ONE

2 Corinthians 6:16-18

16For we are the temple of the living God; just as God said,

"I will dwell in them and walk among them;
And I will be their God, and they shall be My people.
17"Therefore, come out from their midst and be separate," says the Lord.
"And do not touch what is unclean;
And I will welcome you.
18"And I will be a father to you,
And you shall be sons and daughters to Me,"
Says the Lord Almighty.

2 Corinthians 7:1

Therefore having these promises, beloved, let us cleanse ourselves from all defilement of flesh and spirit, perfecting holiness in the fear of God.

GUIDE

Living a distinctive Christian life means that we start living . . . .
(2 Corinthians 7:1)

. . . .

1. There is a . . . .

The defining quality is . . . .

It is not . . . .

2. There is a . . . .

Perfecting means . . . .

Holiness means . . . .

. . . .

How do you know what the right thing to do is? You ask . . . .

. . . .

(Getting to Your Destination Viewing Guide continues of page 85.)

Discussion Questions

1. The defining quality of the Christian life is the presence of God living in us. Do you think your life is distinctive because of Christ? Would others think that?

2. When you ask the question, "Is it holy?," how does it change the way you respond to the issues you face in life?

BECOMING A BELIEVER
GOING THE EXTRA MILE
FOCUSES YOUR PURPOSE

When God moves in, the direction of your life changes. Becoming a believer made you a temple for the living God (see 2 Corinthians. 6:16), and your purpose now has more to do with God, because you belong to Him.

Check out these passages about God's purpose for you.

"And we know that God causes all things to work together for good to those who love God, to those who are called according to His purpose" (Romans 8:28).

"[God] has saved us, and called us with a holy calling, not according to our works, but according to His own purpose and grace which was granted us in Christ Jesus from all eternity" (2 Timothy 1:9).

"Holy brethren, partakers of a heavenly calling" (Hebrews 3:1).

From Romans 8:28, how are we called?

. . . .

In 2 Timothy, how does Paul describe the calling of those who are saved?

. . . .

. . . .

And in Hebrews, how is our calling described?

. . . .

In light of these passages, your life, purpose, and passions can't just be about you anymore! You and I have been called with a heavenly calling. Our lives now have everything to do with heaven, holiness, and God. Being a child of God permeates every part of our being.

DAVE QUOTE

I constantly meet people who have no idea what they want to do with their lives. I ask, "What do you want to do? If there were no limitations of time, money, or education, what would you choose? What is it that stirs you? What is it that feeds your passion?"

Take a few minutes to think about your passions and purpose. What are the passions God put inside of you? What are the things you feel strongly about? What kind of things would you get up early for? List them here.

. . . .

. . . .

. . . .

Can't find anything you feel passionate about? What did you like to do as a child? Have you usually been drawn toward one type of activity? Keep thinking and praying about this if you're having trouble. What you're passionate about probably won't be a new revelation. The thread of your passion has already been woven through most of your life experiences.

How are you already using your passions?

. . . .

. . . .

God's purpose for you won't be something you hate. He wants you working in your strengths, in the things you love to do. Is God's purpose part of your plans? What is your heavenly calling?

. . . .

. . . .

A personal mission statement is a few lines that sum up what you're about and where you believe God is directing your life. Getting something on paper can be helpful for focusing on your purpose. Some people even take personal retreats every year or two to think and pray about what God is doing in their lives.

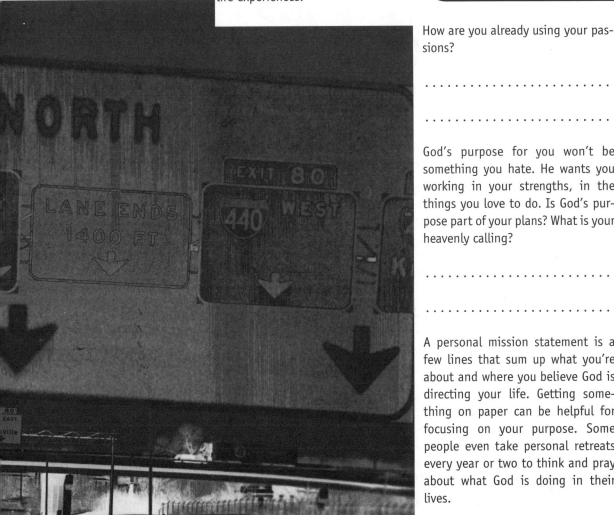

DAVE QUOTE

Most of the Bible people could have had simple mission statements—not a 100-page dissertation. Moses could have said, "I am to deliver Israel." Noah, "I am to build an ark." David, "I am to be king." Joseph, "I am to be a ruler."

Can you fill in the blank?

I am . . . .

. . . .

Make your personal mission statement short and direct. Consider the themes that have consistently run through your life. Those are the areas God is probably leading in.

PRAY for God's leading about His purpose and plan for you. Confess your need to figure it out all by yourself. Ask God to show you what the next steps are.

On a stick of deodorant, it says "not a cover-up." That means that the deodorant doesn't just mask the smell, it actually eliminates it. Holiness is not a cover-up, it's a complete change. The old life is actually eliminated.

DAVE QUOT

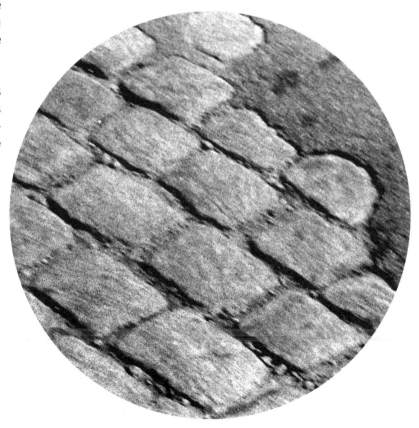

IS IT HOLY?
GOING THE EXTRA MILE
PART ONE

When God is present, our response must be the pursuit of holiness. As we begin to ask "Is it holy?" about every area of our lives, things begin to change. God is unleashed in our lives. The power of the Almighty begins to reign. The right reason to pursue holy living is that you are a Christian, not to make you a Christian. The death of Jesus has freed us from pretending to be holy. Many labor under the wrong reasons to pursue holiness, but because of Jesus, we are freed from:

- The old way of thinking - "Doing right will make me better."
- The guilt - "I've made some mistakes. God must surely be mad at me, so I've got to show Him how good I can be."
- The sense of obligation - "Jesus died for me, so I've got to work, and dig, and gut it out, to hold up my end of the bargain."

Instead, we pursue holiness because of the love relationship we have with the Father. From that love comes a desire to develop holy character.

Developing Holy Character

Holy character comes from holy choices. It is the outgrowth of holiness living inside you. Holy choices protect what's inside you—the presence of God. Holiness begins on the inside. Philippians 1:6 says that God has begun a work in you, and that He will perfect it. It is ongoing, a process, day in and day out. It never stops, even when you're not thinking about it, God is still perfecting the work He has begun.

The aim of holiness is obedience—not just doing stuff, but becoming like Jesus at every level of your life. It takes place through an overhaul or complete change.

Through holiness God:
- Changes our hearts—taking out the old and replacing it with the new.
- Constructs new beliefs—through discipleship, growth, and prayer.
- Creates new behavior—results in new actions and decisions.

Principles of Purity
A pure life brings fertile ground for growing in holiness.

Psalm 101
[1]"I will sing of the lovingkindness and justice,
To Thee, O Lord, I will sing praises,
[2]I will give heed to the blameless way.
When wilt Thou come to me?
I will walk within my house in the integrity of my heart.
[3]I will set no worthless thing before my eyes;
I hate the work of those who fall away;
It shall not fasten its grip on me.
[4]A perverse heart shall depart from me;
I will know no evil.
[5]Whoever secretly slanders his neighbor, him I will destroy;
No one who has a haughty look and an arrogant heart will I endure.
[6]My eyes shall be upon the faithful of the land, that they may dwell with me;
He who walks in a blameless way is the one who will minister to me.
[7]He who practices deceit shall not dwell within my house;

DAVE QUOTE

Tape a card to your TV with Psalm 101: 3 written on it. Remind yourself that what goes into your mind matters.

He who speaks falsehood shall not maintain his position before me.
⁸Every morning I will destroy all the wicked of the land,
So as to cut off from the city of the Lord all those who do iniquity."

In this Psalm, King David is speaking to the Lord. He tells the Lord that he is determined to maintain purity in his empire by removing wickedness from himself and his court.

Purity brings powerful results (v. 1). David experienced God in worship because he took the time to make sure every area of his life was clean. He praised the Lord for His love and justice.

Purity comes out of a positive, passionate relationship with God (v. 2). David resolved to live a pure life, with a blameless heart before God. He was saying, "I will pay attention to the way of purity." He wasn't doing it out of obligation, but out of relationship with God.
A decision based on love is easier to make. If my love for God is real, then it's easier to say no to some things, and yes to the ways of the Lord. Have you ever made a commitment to live a pure life before God?
❑ yes ❑ no

Write your commitment here.

. . . .

. . . .

DAVE QUOTE

Many grocery stores have little flower shops in them. They have refrigerated glass cases where they display the flowers. You can go in there day or night and often find a man standing in front of them. Most often he's standing there because he's done something wrong. They should just have the flowers categorized by the mistakes you've made. This one for a lie. That one if you've cheated. Another one if you've forgotten to call. The man is there out of obligation. Buying the flowers is not really an expression of love. He's made a mistake, and he feels obligated to make up for it as best he can. Many times our pursuit of purity is out of obligation, we're trying to do something to make up for the past, and so our efforts are hit and miss. Purity is consistent when its based on a love relationship with God.

Purity brings protection (vv. 3-7).

Verse 3 says, "I will set no worthless thing before my eyes." What you do and what you watch really matter. What about the TV shows you watch? The movies you go to? Pornography? What kinds of worthless things do you set before your eyes?

. . . .

A commitment to this verse will protect the purity of your mind and heart.

Verse 3 talks about hating the work of those who fall away. How are your business ethics? Do you choose not to deal with those who are crooked or deceitful? Or do you cover up the sin by saying, "it's just business"? To protect the purity of your career and your relationship with God, you have to decide not to deal with the crooked or deceitful.

In verses 4 and 5, David tells the perverse at heart to depart from him. You cannot keep yourself pure if you hang out with people who are evil and perverted. It's the epitome of hypocrisy to align yourself with people who aren't living by the same standards you are. Who do you choose to spend your free time with?

Verse 6 says David surrounded himself with faithful people. People closest to us have a great impact on us. What kind of people are in your life? What does that say about what you're really committed to? Our purity is protected when we surround ourselves with godly and righteous people.

Are the people you're closest to committed to protecting purity?

Are the people who have access to your heart faithful believers?

Do the people who influence your decisions have a passionate relationship with the Lord?

Is there someone you need to distance yourself from in order to grow in your relationship with God?

Verse 7 says that we are not to let the deceitful dwell in our houses. If they aren't in love with Jesus, then you don't have God's permission to date them.

Purity grows when it's practiced (verse 8).

David was committed to destroying anything that threatened his purity—every morning. *Purity* is expressing your love for God in every area of your life. It requires steady application. Each day requires that you continually make the right choices, until it becomes a pattern.

Practical helps for physical purity

1. Don't put yourself in a position or place where you know you're going to fall.
2. Date in groups.
3. Have someone hold you accountable—someone who knows what you're up to and can ask you the hard questions.
4. If you feel like what you're dealing with is beyond you own resources, then get professional help. Don't try to do it alone.

DAVE QUOTE

Women always see guys as fixer-uppers. They look at a guy and go, "Well, I can fix him."

DAVE QUOTE

Purity is not pulling weeds. It's growing roses. It's not just making sure I don't do wrong. It's about making room, so that positive things can be produced. It's about adding positive things to my life. It's not just saying no to a bunch of stuff. It's about saying yes to something that's a lot better.

PRAY for a pure life that would honor and glorify God. Ask God to show you the places that need refining. Give Him permission to do whatever it takes to make you holy.

TRAVEL LOG

1. What principle or truth have you learned about the journey?

. . . .

. . . .

. . . .

. . . .

. . . .

2. What do you feel God is trying to say to you about your journey?

. . . .

. . . .

. . . .

. . . .

. . . .

3. What new steps can you take toward the destination (things to do, things to change, things
   to avoid)?

. . . .

. . . .

. . . .

VIEWING

THE ROAD AHEAD PART ONE

2 Corinthians 6:16-18

[16]For we are the temple of the living God; just as God said,
"I will dwell in them and walk among them;
And I will be their God,
and they shall be My people.
[17]"Therefore, come out from their midst and be separate," says the Lord.
"And do not touch what is unclean;
And I will welcome you.
[18]"And I will be a father to you,
And you shall be sons and daughters to Me,"
Says the Lord Almighty.

2 Corinthians 7:1

Therefore having these promises, beloved, let us cleanse ourselves from all defilement of flesh and spirit, perfecting holiness in the fear of God.

GUIDE

2. There is a deciding question (continued)

Always ask yourself . . . .

It matters how you . . . .

It matters what . . . .

3. There is a . . . .

He waits for us to ask . . . .

When we make the . . . .

God makes the . . . .

To be sold out for God means . . . .

. . . .

Discussion Questions

1. If you could ask God to help you establish purity in one area, what area would that be?

2. What action can you take to deal with areas that don't pass the holiness test?

IS IT HOLY

GOING THE EXTRA MILE

PART TWO

Asking, "Is it holy?" is the practical application of becoming holy. Holiness is a process. It's a long journey. A marathon. And for our superficial world that believes in instant satisfaction, the pursuit of holiness seems irrelevant. We desperately need a generation of people who are willing to forsake instant gratification and go deep. Not spiritual giants, but ordinary human beings who want to know God at a deeper level. To pursue holiness means that you move from surface living to depth. It's not about drudgery, but joy. Growing up spiritually means that you aren't so interested in yourself anymore. There is freedom in not being obsessed with self.

All through the Bible, God has outlined ways to get to know Him, different means of entering into His presence. These ways to meet God are called spiritual disciplines. Prayer, Scripture study, meditation, journaling, confession, fasting, and worship are some of the disciplines.

We need practical instruction about how to meet with God. There is no big secret here. We will be beginners all our lives. The primary requirement is that you long to be holy, and that you long to know God. David says in Psalm 42:1-2:

> As the deer pants for the water brooks,
> So my soul pants for Thee, O God.
> My soul thirsts for God, for the living God;
> When shall I come and appear before God?

Let's look closely at two of the spiritual disciplines.

Scripture Study

Most all Christians say that they want to hear from God. They want to know what He is saying to them. Yet, they neglect to read what God has already written to them. The Bible is God's primary means of speaking to us. From the Word, you get to know who you are in Christ—your identity. You have to know who you are, believe it, and begin to live it out.

The Bible is the road map that guides this journey, and studying the Word should be a consistent discipline. It's possible that if you're feeling lost, it's because you haven't checked the map in a while.

People come up to me and ask my advice about something, whether it's how to know God's will, or how to be forgiven. I'll give them a Scripture-based response, and they'll say, "Oh yeah, I know that." I'll go, "So what's the problem?" The problem is, they know it, but it hasn't affected their lives.

DAVE QUOTE

DAVE QUOTE

If you're dealing with a subject, let's say worry, then look the word up in the concordance and read everything about it. Even if you don't know much about the Bible, or a subject, look it up and find out everything you can about it. Don't be afraid to jump in.

DAVE QUOTE

I meet so many people who are intimidated by the Bible—too many pages, big, hard words, they don't know where to start, unfamiliar imagery and characters, they get paralyzed. But you can do this. The Bible is something that can be read and understood. It doesn't exist to make you feel like a failure. You can approach it like you would a friend who has the answers. It will benefit you. It gives you direction, protection, and wisdom.

Look at some of the benefits of studying the Bible:

Knowing God's Word will help us be successful.
" 'This book of the law shall not depart from your mouth, but you shall meditate on it day and night, so that you may be careful to do according to all that is written in it; for then you will make your way prosperous, and then you will have success' " (Joshua 1:8).

How would you define success?

. . . .

. . . .

Knowing God's Word equips us for good work.
"All Scripture is inspired by God and profitable for teaching, for reproof, for correction, for training in righteousness; that the man of God may be adequate, equipped for every good work" (2 Timothy 3:16-17).

As a Christian, how will the Bible equip you?

. . . .

Knowing God's Word will keep our motives pure.
"For the word of God is living and active and sharper than any two-edged sword, and piercing as far as the division of soul and spirit, of both joints and marrow, and able to judge the thoughts and intentions of the heart" (Hebrews 4:12).

Do you sometimes question, "Am I hearing God, or just listening to my selfish desires?" Where can you go for discernment?

. . . .

Knowing God's Word will help us grow spiritually.
"Like newborn babes, long for the pure milk of the word, that by it you may grow in respect to salvation" (1 Peter 2:2).

How is a baby like a new Christian?

. . . .

. . . .

Knowing God's Word will keep us from sin.
Thy word I have treasured in my heart, ____ That I may not sin against Thee (Psalm 119:11).

How could memorizing God's Word keep you from sin?

. . . .

. . . .

Knowing God's Word will give us wisdom.

My son, if you will receive my sayings,
And treasure my commandments within you,
Make your ear attentive to wisdom,
Incline your heart to understanding;
For if you cry for discernment,
Lift your voice for understanding;
If you seek her as silver,
And search for her as for hidden treasures;
Then you will discern the fear of the Lord,
And discover the knowledge of God.
For the Lord gives wisdom;
From His mouth come knowledge and understanding (Proverbs 2:1-6).

What are the conditions for receiving God's wisdom?

. . . .

. . . .

. . . .

DAVE QUOTE

If you're dealing with a subject, let's say worry, then look the word up in the concordance and read everything about it. Even if you don't know much about the Bible, or a subject, look it up and find out everything you can about it. Don't be afraid to jump in.

What would it take for you to become a person who reads the Bible more?

. . . .

. . . .

. . . .

DAVE QUOTE

I meet so many people who are intimidated by the Bible—too many pages, big, hard words, they don't know where to start, unfamiliar imagery and characters, they get paralyzed. But you can do this. The Bible is something that can be read and understood. It doesn't exist to make you feel like a failure. You can approach it like you would a friend who has the answers. It will benefit you. It gives you direction, protection, and wisdom.

Prayer

Prayer is one of the most central spiritual disciplines. It ushers us into communion with the Father. When we pray, we change. It is the main avenue God uses to transform our lives. Have you ever noticed that when you're unwilling to change and don't really care what God has to say, then you abandon your prayer life? Through our prayers, God is faithful to meet us right where we are and slowly move us on to deeper things. The power to live a holy life is already inside you because of Jesus, and prayer is the means by which we tap into that power.

Let's use the acrostic PRAY to remember how to pray.

P - is for praise.

Shout joyfully to the Lord, all the earth.
Serve the Lord with gladness;
Come before Him with joyful singing.
Know that the Lord Himself is God;
It is He who has made us, and not we ourselves;
We are His people and the sheep of His pasture.
Enter His gates with thanksgiving,
And His courts with praise.
Give thanks to Him; bless His name.
For the Lord is good;
His lovingkindness is everlasting,
And His faithfulness to all generations (Psalm 100).

At the beginning of your prayer time, spend some time in praise. Call out who God has been to you. What makes your life rock? Thank the Lord for all that's good. Worship Him.

Spend some time now praising God for who He is and His faithfulness to you.

R - is for repent.

"If we confess our sins, He is faithful and righteous to forgive us our sins and to cleanse us from all unrighteousness" (1 John 1:9).

Why is it so difficult to confess our sin to God? God promises that when we confess, He will forgive and cleanse. Spend the next part of your prayer time in confession and repentance. *Repentance* is turning from your sin and choosing a different path. Do that in God's presence.

Confess your behaviors, thoughts, and attitudes that aren't Christ-like. Ask God for the strength and wisdom to respond and choose differently next time.

A - is anything for anybody.

"Pray for one another, so that you may be healed. The effective prayer of a righteous man can accomplish much" (James 5:16).

Praying for someone else is called *intercession*. You are speaking to the Father on behalf of someone you care about. When Jesus and the apostles prayed for others, they prayed boldly with strength and authority. You do not have to pray half-hearted, wishy-washy prayers.

Make a list of the people you would consistently like to pray for. Pray through your list. Add others who ask for your prayers.

Y - is for yourself.

"Be anxious for nothing, but in everything by prayer and supplication with thanksgiving let your requests be made known to God. And the peace of God, which surpasses all comprehension, shall guard your hearts and your minds in Christ Jesus" (Philippians 4:6-7).

Save your needs for last and cover all your personal requests with "if it be Thy will." The great yearning of our hearts is to know the will of God. This type of prayer will permeate every life experience. Sometimes when you pray for yourself, you will sense that your own will is in conflict with the will and way of God. When God brings it up, it's time to deal with it and let go of whatever stands between you and God.

Finish your prayer time with the freedom of bringing all your needs and worries before God.

We know God always answers our prayers. Romans 8:28 says He is working all things for our good. He will answer your prayers in one of three ways:

No - the request is wrong, or not in line with the will of God.
Maybe - the timing is wrong, or maybe your heart isn't right.
Yes -it's all good; everything is on go.

What are some examples of *no, maybe,* and *yes* answers you have received?

. . . .

. . . .

. . . .

What would it take for you to become a person who prays more?

. . . .

. . . .

. . . .

. . . .

DAVE QUOTE

Someone once told me this about prayer: PUSH - pray until something happens.

THE DELIBERATE QUEST

GOING THE EXTRA MILE

The bottom line on the journey, and pursuing holiness, is that you have to choose. You have to make a conscious choice and consistent effort to choose the right path and stick with it. The Proverbs 2 passage we looked at earlier says that if you study God's Word, cry out for discernment, and seek God, then you will know God. Commitment is mandatory if you want to grow. Your heart and mind have to be engaged. God will give you every opportunity. He's put up street lights, flashing neon signs, written out the directions, given you a travel companion, and outlined the destination; but He won't choose the road for you. That's where love comes in. God knows that if He forces you, it won't be a true love relationship.

Ever had anyone fall for you that you weren't interested in? They begin to call, send you cards, and turn up everywhere. They decide to do anything to get you to love them. It's awful. You just want to run and hide. God won't force you to love Him like that. He doesn't want manipulated love. But when you

You have to choose! God won't make you do anything. God will lead you, but you have to choose. It is a deliberate quest. You have to do something. I hear all the time, "Well, I prayed and God didn't do anything." Really? It might be because He's waiting for you to take action. To get out of an ungodly relationship, you actually have to say the words, "it's over." Godliness is a choice, marriage is a choice, happiness is a choice, purity is a choice, holiness is a choice. At this point, it's about effort and commitment.

DAVE QUOTE

choose to love, when your heart goes crazy and you've totally fallen, then love is sweet and tender and good. That's the love relationship God wants with you. God wants you to desire His presence. He wants you to want holiness and purity. God wants you to choose, because when you do, the relationship will be honest and true.

"Do you not know that those who run in a race all run, but only one receives the prize? Run in such a way that you may win. And everyone who competes in the games exercises self-control in all things. They then do it to receive a perishable wreath, but we an imperishable. Therefore, I run in such a way, as not without aim; I box in such a way, as not beating the air; but I buffet my body and make it my slave, lest possibly, after I have preached to others, I myself should be disqualified" (1 Corinthians 9:24-27).

The journey is not a 100-yard dash; it's a marathon. Reaching the destination is a spiritual race that we all can win. We only lose by choice. Everyone wants the prize, but no one wants the process. If you truly want to pursue God, and if you truly want to be holy, what's stopping you? Hebrews 12 says:

"Therefore, since we have so great a cloud of witnesses surrounding us, let us also lay aside every encumbrance, and the sin which so easily entangles us, and let us run with endurance the race that is set before us, fixing our eyes on Jesus, the author and perfecter of faith, who for the joy set before Him endured the cross, despising the shame, and has sat down at the right hand of the throne of God" (Hebrews 12:1-2).

To pursue holiness means you deliberately set aside the encumbrances that hold you back. Some of the most common ones are:

- Spiritual mediocrity - No one suddenly becomes base. It's like erosion that happens over time. There's no noise, just every once in a while a piece falls off.
- Sin and lack of repentance - It's impossible to grow without a continuing repentant attitude. Jeremiah 17:9 says the heart is deceitful above all things.
- Ungodly relationships - Who do you spend your time with? Who has access to your heart? Do they push you toward Jesus? Proverbs 4:23 warns, "Watch over your heart with all diligence, for from it flow the springs of life."

Where are you most easily entangled? What is keeping you from running the race with endurance?

. . . .

. . . .

. . . .

To run and win, you must break away from the herd. If normal is heathen, then abnormal is probably holy. To "run in such a way that you may win," means you will probably be called to be different than those around you, maybe even different from the Christians around you.

In what ways is God calling you to be different?

. . . .

. . . .

Pray, committing to God that you will deliberately choose holiness. In His presence, set aside the encumbrances that entangle you. Ask God where He is calling you to be different. Trust Him for the strength for endurance.

"Not that I have already obtained it, or have already become perfect, but I press on in order that I may lay hold of that for which also I was laid hold of by Christ Jesus. Brethren, I do not regard myself as having laid hold of it yet; but one thing I do: forgetting what lies behind and reaching forward to what lies ahead, I press on toward the goal for the prize of the upward call of God in Christ Jesus" (Philippians 3:12-14).

And so, no matter what, press on. Let go of all that's behind you and fix your eyes on the destination. Whatever it takes, however slow you run, don't forsake the journey. Whatever the cost, who cares what everyone else says, press on. The Savior waits ready to welcome you home and shout with all of heaven, **"Well done, my good and faithful servant."**

1. What principle or truth have you learned about the journey?

. . . .

. . . .

. . . .

. . . .

. . . .

2. What do you feel God is trying to say to you about your journey?

. . . .

. . . .

. . . .

. . . .

. . . .

3. What new steps can you take toward the destination (things to do, things to change, things to avoid)?

. . . .

. . . .

. . . .

DESTINATION
NOTES

DESTINATION NOTES

DESTINATION NOTES